DISCARD

Buna Rubber

THE BIRTH OF AN INDUSTRY

Buna Rubber

THE BIRTH OF AN INDUSTRY

by

FRANK A. HOWARD

1947

D. VAN NOSTRAND COMPANY, INC.

NEW YORK

TO

The Chemical Engineer
who translates advances
in chemical science into
new industries.

PREFACE

This is the story of the synthetic rubber industry, carrying with it some intertwined lengths out of the histories of other new industries.

New industries are the result of two life processes of civilization, the continuous increase in the sum of human knowledge by discovery and research, and the new application of human knowledge by invention and practical development work. In earlier times new industries came into being either by the slow processes of evolution, or through the efforts of promoters. London was the financial center of the world, and in the City they had a simple formula for such things—the time to invest in a new industry was after the third reorganization. It was an historic fact that many new industries had been built on the financial remains of successive layers of ruined shareholders. But by the end of the first World War it had been shown that if scientists, engineers, and experienced production men worked as a team and with adequate financial resources, profits could be made out of new industrial developments. Conservative business everywhere began organizing itself to seek new inventions and carry out research and development work for the advancement of old industries and the creation of new ones.

Science and technology have no geographical borders. The horizons of this work were necessarily world-wide. Each nation borrowed or bought what it needed from abroad and tried to make the best use of it at home.

With the coming of the second World War several of the new American industries which had resulted from these industrial research programs came to maturity just in time to meet our needs. Perhaps the most important of all was the production of synthetic rubber of which the Baruch Committee said: "if we fail to secure quickly a large new rubber supply our war effort and our domestic economy both will collapse."

During the early stages of the building of this most critical and complex of the new war industries, it became the subject of prolonged public controversy. The evolution of heat in this controversy, while considerable, was of no lasting importance in itself. But out of the fires of the rubber controversy there arose an active public interest in the new industry and in basic principles of international relations in the industrial field.

In studying these questions we are dealing with a living society, the American republic, which must adapt itself to existence in a world filled with competing societies. If we are to maintain the highest standard of living in this competitive world, we must continue to create new industries and expand the field of usefulness of our existing industries. Our American society has in it an urge and a genius for creative effort along these practical lines which is now unequaled anywhere. But it also has its own weaknesses.

The best method of studying such problems is probably the "case history" method. It therefore seemed that the story of the synthetic rubber industry might serve a useful purpose, not only to amplify the record on an interesting chapter of American history, but also because it will throw some light of experience on national issues which may be debated in the future.

F. A. H.

CONTENTS

INTRODUCTION

I first became acquainted with the author of this book, Frank Howard, when in World War I both of us found ourselves in Washington exerting ourselves to the utmost to aid the Allies with any scientific knowledge which we had that might be made applicable to the pressing problems confronting the armed forces. As a result of this acquaintance, at the close of the war Professor Ira Remsen, ex-President of Johns Hopkins University, and Mr. Howard came to me to ask for my assistance in some of the problems of the petroleum industry in which they were engaged, and for a few years thereafter I saw much of Mr. Howard's own activities and found in him a man of high character, fertile scientific imagination, and of penetrating intelligence, both in petroleum science and in law. It was because of this association that I had some little familiarity with the negotiations carried on by Mr. Teagle and Mr. Howard on behalf of the Standard Oil Company of New Jersey, and Dr. Carl Bosch of Germany, Nobel prize winner in chemistry for 1930, on behalf of the "I. G. Farbenindustrie." For all three of these men I developed a very high admiration.

I have had the opportunity to look over the proof sheets of this book, and am sure that the history which it narrates comes from the pen of one who knows more about that history than any living person. It therefore represents a contribution of great interest and value to both petroleum and rubber chemistry, as well as to the understanding of the political and scientific developments which were intimately connected with both World War I and World War II.

The factual attitude and the scientific objectivity which

Mr. Howard has maintained throughout his narrative, in particular his entire freedom from caustic criticism in spite of the fact that the book lies in two highly controversial fields, international big business and governmental administration, gives it a unique value as a case history in these fields. It is written with a detachment extraordinarily rare for anybody who was so active a participant in the developments which it narrates. In it Mr. Howard appears not in the role of a propagandist. He is clearly concerned only with getting a factual account of a critical chapter in the evolution of our present-day world.

ROBERT A. MILLIKAN

November 27, 1946.

CHAPTER I

RUBBER

My late friend, Thomas Midgley, Jr., one of America's great industrial research leaders of the era between the first and second world wars, tried hard in behalf of General Motors Corporation to achieve a commercial synthesis of rubber. Perhaps because he had been first trained as an engineer,* Midgley always reduced his chemical concepts to mechanical images and, during his long and fruitless search for a good synthetic rubber, he evolved a homely statement of the essentials of rubber chemistry.

According to Midgley, rubber is any soft plastic material which will stretch. It stretches because it is elastic. This soft elasticity, unlike the hard elasticity of steel, comes from long coiled molecules interlaced in tangled masses like curled horsehair. If you pull or push too hard, the turns and coils in these tangled masses slip and the rubber takes a permanent set instead of merely opening and closing its internal coils.

In natural rubber the long coils are actually made up of simpler units of a substance called *isoprene*, which in its pure form is a clear liquid much like naphtha. The process of causing simple molecules to form long chains is known as polymerization. In some way the rubber tree builds up a polymer of isoprene in a special body-fluid of the tree called "latex"— a fluid which circulates only in the bark and is quite distinct

---

* Although a mechanical engineer by training Midgley worked almost exclusively in chemical fields, and at the time of his death, in November, 1944, was President of the American Chemical Society. He was the father of Ethyl fluid for treating gasoline and created the refrigerant Freon on which most domestic refrigeration and air conditioning plants depend.

from the tree's sap. When the water is dried out of this latex, the long chains of isoprene are left behind, intertwined with one another to form the soft plastic mass which we call crude rubber.

In 1839, Charles Goodyear discovered that if rubber is heated with sulphur it becomes much tougher and loses its tendency to "slip" internally. It acts as though the sulphur molecules had stitched together the turns and coils of the long rubber molecule chains wherever they came closest together in the tangled mass. They may tear, but will no longer "slip," no matter how much they are pulled or pushed.

The "natural" rubber which the world used happened, then, to be made out of isoprene polymer cross-stitched with sulphur. But the fact that the links of the polymer chains were molecules of isoprene was only an accident of nature. There might be many other kinds of molecules besides isoprene which could be joined in these coiled chains and worked into matted masses to produce soft, elastic, solid bodies; and instead of sulphur there might be many other things which could be used for cross-stitching. On these assumptions of Midgley's, it seemed that rubber of many different kinds, some perhaps much better than the natural product, might be made synthetically.

I first saw a piece of synthetic rubber almost immediately after I joined the Standard Oil Company (N.J.) organization in October, 1919. Neither in "life" nor in strength was this synthetic rubber at all equal to the natural material. But it was a soft plastic material which would stretch and, by Midgley's homely definition as well as by the more conventional reasoning of organic chemists, it actually was rubber of a sort.

Dr. Clarence I. Robinson, then Standard Oil's chief chemist, had been abroad early in the year visiting the Company's European refineries for the first time since 1914. The desperate last years of the first World War, he found, had reduced the German oil industry to a shadow. Like a starving man, it had been trying, with the aid of chemistry, to live on anything it could find. The rubber industry had been even harder hit, if possible, than oil. There was absolutely no crude rubber available, and rubber was desperately needed, not only for tires but also for electrical insulation, for balloon fabrics, for hose, for engine packing—in fact, for almost every piece of industrial, marine, naval or air equipment.

Germany's success in meeting this problem, at least to a small extent, by producing several tons of synthetic rubber a day during 1917 and 1918 was regarded at that time as an outstanding chemical achievement. Dr. Robinson was able to obtain a sample in 1919, and this he brought back and showed to me in October of that year. He was not sure of the origin of the sample, but he believed it was from synthetic rubber made by the Badische Anilin und Soda Fabrik of Ludwigshafen-am-Rhein.

This first German synthetic rubber was not the same chemically as natural rubber. The Germans had chosen as their raw material *dimethyl butadiene*, a hydrocarbon molecule closely akin to isoprene. They had apparently developed at least three different techniques to polymerize these molecules into long chains resembling natural rubber. The synthetic rubbers produced were called *methyl rubber*. One technique produced a tire rubber; another, a rubber for hard molded products such as battery boxes; and the third, for fine products such as wire insulation for airplane magnetos and coatings for balloon fabric.

The "rubber" of Dr. Robinson's sample, which was examined in Standard's Bayway research laboratories in 1919, was so bad that we could well believe the stories that solid tires made of it had to be jacked up at night in cold weather to prevent them from developing flat spots where they rested on the ground. But it was, historically, the seed of the Buna synthetic rubber which kept the wheels of civilization turning twenty-five years later.

It was also about this time that America first became conscious of rubber as a national problem.

Brazil had been the original rubber supplier for the United States. Rubber trees grew wild in the Brazilian jungles. They were tapped much as Vermont sugar maple trees are tapped, and the latex collected. Crude rubber was derived from the latex in the most primitive way by dipping a stick in the liquid and then drying it over a fire. At each dip the coating grew thicker, until finally a pear-shaped mass about the size of a football was formed on the stick. From these beginnings the Brazilian rubber trade had grown into one of the bonanza industries of the New World during the nineteenth century.

Sir Henry Wickham, an English coffee planter and amateur botanist, took some rubber seeds from Brazil to London in 1876. There at Kew Gardens the first artificially propagated rubber trees matured. From London, seedlings went first to Ceylon, and then the following year from Ceylon to Singapore and other parts of the Malay Peninsula, where English colonists were endeavoring to develop new exports. The trees thrived in the climate of Malaya and spread throughout the East. By 1907 rubber from Far East plantations had gained a foothold in the market and was supplying 5 per cent of the world demand.

The British development in the Malay Peninsula had been watched with interest by the Dutch colonials in the nearby East Indies, and soon they followed the British. From that time the Brazilian production of wild rubber, upon which the entire industry had been founded, dwindled until it became a negligible factor in the market. The growth of the automobile industry and the ingenuity of rubber goods manufacturers in finding new uses for rubber were creating demands which the Amazon Valley could never hope to supply. The maximum output of these jungles was, in 1912, 41,600 tons. By 1925 the world's rubber requirement was more than 500,000 tons and the Brazilian output had dropped to 25,298 tons.

The mushroom-like growth of the market, the shift of the sources of supply from the Brazilian jungles to the British plantations—and then in part to the Dutch plantations—produced a chaotic market. Between 1914 and 1922 the price of crude rubber ranged from 11½ cents to $1.02 per pound. Fast as the market was expanding, it could not always keep up with the output of the rapidly growing plantations. It seemed impossible to keep supply and demand in balance, and profits in the rubber goods industry became more a matter of shrewd speculation than of efficient manufacture.

This was the background for the first direct governmental intervention in the rubber industry, the Stevenson Plan.

This plan was the outgrowth of efforts by the British rubber planters to obtain governmental aid in stabilizing the chaotic market. The Stevenson Committee, appointed by the British Colonial Office, recommended control of rubber output in Malaya and Ceylon. The Netherlands Indies government was asked to participate with the British, but it had ambitions for a much greater share of the market and was unwilling to accept a quota fixed by its existing plantations. The control program became effective November 1, 1922, and continued in force until November 1, 1928. Each plantation's ability to produce was determined and exportable percentages were declared quarterly on a basis determined by the London market price for rubber. Growers were given export coupons which amounted to licensing exports and indirectly restricted production. The plan raised the price of rubber, but it did not operate well enough to balance production with consumption, and in 1925 a shortage developed which put prices up to $1.12 a pound in New York.

By this time the United States was consuming 76 per cent of the world's total output of rubber. Its automobile industry was growing at a tremendous rate. Tires were serviceable but not too good. They were running perhaps 10,000 miles, somewhat more than a year of service for the average motorist. At $1.00 per pound for crude rubber it might cost the car owner $200 a year to keep tires on his car.

That threat was too much. Rubber became a national problem.

Herbert Hoover, then Secretary of Commerce, inveighed against such intervention in world trade by foreign governments. In effect he served notice upon the British that if the Stevenson Plan remained in force, this country would try to protect itself in every possible way.

Thomas A. Edison undertook to discover or develop some alternative source of rubber supply. He examined thousands of plants from all over the world in an effort to find one which could be domesticated in the United States as a substitute for the rubber tree. General Motors Corporation asked Thomas Midgley, Jr., to undertake a research program on synthetic rubber, and Henry Ford investigated the possibilities for the cultivation of rubber in Brazil. Harvey S. Firestone, Sr., one of the great tire manufacturers, started a rubber plantation in Liberia, but there were many adverse conditions to meet and it was generally recognized that the development would be slow and uphill. The United States Rubber Company and the Goodyear Tire and Rubber Company adopted more direct measures of commercial protection by developing their own plantations in Malaya and Sumatra, and Goodyear also made a start in Central America.

But nothing much came of any of these attempts to develop American-controlled rubber production. Even the American companies who were most active in establishing plantations were never able to produce more than a fraction of their own rubber requirements, and the General Motors research program on synthetic rubber failed to bring any practical results, although Midgley had obtained some interesting new data.

But the control of America's rubber supply by the British colonies was being loosened at the very time the Stevenson Plan went into effect, and was completely broken soon afterward, by the expanding plantations of the Dutch colonies. Again the price of rubber came down to reasonable levels, and rubber, as a national problem, vanished from the American consciousness.

However, with the world depression of the 1930's, rubber markets again became chaotic, this time making new records for *low* prices. Crude rubber reached an all-time low of 2.7 cents a pound in the New York market, and the idea of governmental restriction of production and exports was quietly resurrected under the pressure of these ruinous prices. This time the plan included all the large plantation areas, Malaya, Ceylon, Netherlands Indies, Burma, India, State of North Borneo, Sarawak, Siam and French Indo-China—97 per cent of the total production.

Out of this new effort came, in 1934, the International Rubber Regulation Agreement, administered by a governing committee made up of delegates from each of the East Indies rubber-producing colonies and states. The agreement was well publicized at the time and, in an effort to forestall criticism, it provided for representatives of consumers who were to act in an advisory capacity. Two of these represented American consumers.

The new plan worked. It accomplished its intended purpose from 1934 until the Japanese conquest of this entire rubber-producing area (except Ceylon and India) in 1942. During that period production was held even with demand, the price of crude rubber advanced quickly from its low point and then moved only in moderate swings within a range satisfactory to the growers and their governments.

The record of natural rubber prices which reflects the troubled youth and the perhaps too well disciplined later years of this commodity, was as follows:

NEW YORK PRICE FOR PLANTATION
RIBBED SMOKED SHEETS *

	Year	Highest Price	Lowest Price	Average
	1923......	35.6	25.3	29.5
Period	1924......	38.5	18.5	26.2
of	1925......	112.0	35.0	72.5
Stevenson	1926......	85.5	36.0	48.5
Plan	1927......	41.5	33.0	37.7
	1928......	37.5	16.5	22.5
	1929......	24.4	16.1	20.5
Period	1930......	15.8	8.1	11.9
of Free	1931......	8.2	4.6	6.1
Market	1932......	4.5	2.7	3.4
	1933......	8.8	2.9	5.9
	1934......	15.5	9.9	12.9
Period of	1935......	13.2	11.4	12.3
Inter-	1936......	20.0	14.9	16.4
national	1937......	24.1	14.6	19.4
Rubber	1938......	16.9	11.6	14.7
Regula-	1939......	21.5	15.8	17.7
tion	1940......	22.1	19.1	20.1
Agreement	1941......	23.1	19.9	22.4
	1942......	22.5	22.5	22.5
	1943......	22.5	22.5	22.5

* Figures from U.S. Tariff Commission Report No. 6, September, 1944.

While this second control plan operated smoothly as these figures show, it could not be said to have been entirely satisfactory to the consumers of rubber. There is no record of official criticism at the time, but in a retrospective review made in 1946, the Inter-Agency Policy Committee on Rubber of the Government of the United States described the control plans as follows:

The operation of the two control schemes was disadvantageous to the interest of the United States. There were no adequate safeguards for the consumer's interest in low prices and efficient production, for the rubber goods manufacturer's interest in stable prices of raw materials, nor for the broad national interest in the maintenance of adequate stocks against a time of emergency.†

† First report of Inter-Agency Policy Committee on Rubber, Mr. W. S. Batt, Chairman, February 19, 1946.

Chapter II

OIL FROM COAL

The stream of fate which carried to America two of Germany's greatest scientific achievements, first the production of synthetic oil and then, in the nick of time, the production of synthetic rubber, had its origin far back in the history of America's foreign trade.

Years before there was any need to think of a substitute for natural oil or rubber, America's largest oil company was doing business in Germany. At first it merely sold refined oils to German importing houses. In 1890 it organized with one of these houses a jointly owned company, Deutsche-Amerikanische Petroleum Gesellschaft of Hamburg. This company, called D.A.P.G. for short, became the German agent and distributor for the oil products of the American refineries. The German interests were bought out from time to time and by the end of 1904 the Americans were sole owners of the company.

In the years immediately after the first World War Standard began to receive from representatives in Germany reports of new scientific developments relating to oil. A young chemical engineer from our new industrial research organization, Ross H. Dickson, went over to study this German research. It was clear from his reports that leading chemical companies in Germany—particularly Badische Anilin und Soda Fabrik—were working on many new and interesting processes. So far as oil was concerned, the most important were the distillation of oil from brown coal and the Bergius Process for converting coal directly into oil. The Bergius Process, invented by Dr. Friedrich Bergius * just before the first World War, was extremely simple in theory. Powdered coal was subjected to the action of hydrogen gas at high pressures and temperatures. A part of the coal substance was thus converted into a liquid resembling crude oil. But the practical difficulties in making any commercial use of the process were so great that despite the urgent German need for oil during the war, it had never been possible to operate on an industrial scale.

One afternoon in the spring of 1925 I received at Standard's research laboratories in New Jersey a telephone call from an American friend who had spent several years in Europe in the chemical business. He informed me that some of the directors of the Badische Anilin und Soda Fabrik, whom he had known in Europe, were now in New York on a sight-seeing tour and wished to visit American industrial plants. Would it be possible for them to see Standard's New Jersey oil refineries, which were among the largest in the country? I remembered the synthetic rubber sample, which was still in my desk, and was very curious about the personalities of the men who directed an organization which could really make such products. I referred the question of their visit at once to the Board of Directors of the company, and suggested that in view of Mr. Dickson's reports on the very active German scientific research in the oil business, it might be desirable for them to take this opportunity to meet the Badische directors.

This suggestion was approved and after a day and a half touring the three great refineries on New York Harbor, the German directors were luncheon guests of Standard's directors at the company dining room at 26 Broadway. The difference in language interposed some barrier but the two sets of directors met on the common ground of life-long industrial management experience. The Board of the Badische Com-

* Dr. Bergius received the Nobel Prize for this contribution to science in 1931.

pany, like that of Standard, was made up of men who had grown up in the business.* Dr. Wilhelm Gaus, a South-German chemist who was the senior Badische director, made us a farewell speech in his halting English. He had been much impressed not only by the size and efficiency of the refineries but also by Standard's new organization for industrial research and by the results of its first years of work which we had shown him. He said his own company had been working for some time on important scientific developments relating to the oil industry, and that he would be glad to have me visit their laboratories at Ludwigshafen during my trip to Europe the following year.

In October, 1925, Standard heard again from the Badische Company. Dr. Herman Schmitz, their financial director, and later their chairman, called on one of Standard's European managers in Zurich. He confirmed the reports that Badische had been working on a plan to produce oil from the German brown-coal deposits and said that they also contemplated engaging in the distribution and sale of these oil products in Germany. For that reason they had arranged to buy the Gasolin A.G., a German distributing company which had been a part of the Hugo Stinnes industrial empire and which had been thrown on the market with the collapse of the Stinnes fortune. Dr. Schmitz asked if Standard's subsidiary in Germany would be interested in joining in the Gasolin A.G. purchase with the understanding that it would be used as an additional outlet for American gasoline in Germany as well as for the distribution of oil that Badische might produce from their brown coal. Standard's European manager recommended the purchase on the ground that the price was very attractive and that it was a logical step for Standard, then a leading importer

---

* Under German law corporations such as Badische had a Management Board or "Vorstand" composed of operating executives and a Shareholders' Committee or "Aufsichsrat" composed of stockholders and their financial advisers. The Aufsichsrat met only at long intervals to fix policies, declare dividends and elect the Vorstand.

of gasoline into Germany. The purchase by Standard's German subsidiary of the interest in the Gasolin A.G. was completed in March, 1926, and thus there was established an indirect business connection between Standard and the German chemical industry.

Shortly before this, Dr. Gaus had sent word that the Badische directors would be glad to have me visit Ludwigshafen as soon as convenient. I was just then arranging to go to London, but changed my plans to go directly to Germany instead.

I arrived at Mannheim on March 28, 1926. This city, at the juncture of the Rhine and Neckar rivers almost directly east of Paris, was at that time a large and pleasant industrial metropolis. Between the Rhine and the French border lay the fertile plains of the Rhine Palatinate and the disputed mining province of the Saar. On the west bank of the Rhine, across from Mannheim, was Ludwigshafen, main production and technical center of the Badische company. The French army still occupied the Rhineland, and bridges between Mannheim and Ludwigshafen were patrolled by French troops. The main works, offices and laboratories of the Badische company at Ludwigshafen were all in the French zone of occupation. The Badische therefore maintained a general office in Mannheim and a small executive office in the ancient university town of Heidelberg, some ten miles up the Neckar river.

At Ludwigshafen I was plunged into a world of research and development on a gigantic scale such as I had never seen. The Badische was one of the largest, oldest and most successful chemical companies in the world. The management had had time to balance the cost of new industries against the earnings which they produced, and had reached the conclusion that sound industrial research was the most profitable of all their investments.

With this background and policy the company had undertaken to convert coal into oil. They had chosen as the point of attack the direct addition of hydrogen to coal, the operation shown to be possible by Bergius but never successfully industrialized. The fact to be faced was that before an industry could be built up based on making oil out of coal, new scientific discoveries and much development work were needed. First, and most important, some means had to be found to make the reaction go faster. More of the coal had to be converted to oil more quickly.

When a chemist wishes to speed up a reaction, he has, generally speaking, three ways to turn: he can increase the temperature; he can increase the pressure or concentration of the reacting materials; most useful of all, he can try to find a substance which will act as a "middleman" to bring the reacting substances into the most intimate contact and thus facilitate their union or interaction. The "middleman" is called a *catalyst*.

Badische had found catalysts that would work successfully. They were cheap, hardy and long-lived. Especially, they were immune to the disease which had proved fatal to all such catalysts previously tried—sulphur poisoning. These new catalysts thrived on sulphur, an impurity always found in oil and coals, and if there was not enough sulphur present to meet their appetites, more was added.

This was really a new race of catalysts—catalysts which not only caused hydrogen to unite with coal to convert it into oil, but also caused heavy oil to decompose and simultaneously react with hydrogen to make gasoline or kerosene or diesel fuel. With these catalysts and hydrogen, inferior grades of crude oils or coal tars could be converted entirely into high-quality gasoline. Operations had first been proven on a laboratory scale. From there they had been carried forward through increasingly large units which were already in use at the time of my first visit. There were hydrogen reactors 30 feet high, operating at pressures of 3000 pounds per square inch, and internal temperatures up to a visible red heat.

I spent a day surveying these laboratories and experimental installations at Ludwigshafen, returned early to my hotel, and wrote a brief report which I forwarded at once to Paris where I knew that Mr. Walter C. Teagle, President of the Company, and some of Standard's other senior executives were visiting at the time. I urged that they join me at the earliest date.

A few days later we met in the lovely medieval town of Heidelberg and sat down together there to ponder the effect the startling scientific developments at Ludwigshafen, ten miles away, would have on the world's oil industry.

Two things seemed clear.

The first was that if the worst types of crude oil and tar could be converted entirely into gasoline, the oil industry would no longer need to worry about having its products get out of balance with demand.

The amount of gasoline naturally present in crude oil is relatively small. By the simple distillation methods used in the early days of the industry to separate the crude oil into its component fractions, four barrels of crude were required to produce less than one barrel of gasoline. So long as the principal product sought from oil was kerosene, the amount of gasoline obtained did not greatly matter. Actually, some of it had been dumped as waste. But invention of the automobile and the electric light changed the situation. The need for kerosene declined, while the demand for gasoline increased constantly. About 1911, Dr. William N. Burton of the Standard Oil Company (Indiana) developed the first practical process for application of heat and pressure to crude oil to crack some of its large molecules into the smaller, lighter molecules of gasoline. The Burton process and the later more highly developed cracking processes turned out a barrel of gasoline from about two barrels of crude.

But it was apparent that this might be inadequate. At the rate the automobile industry was growing, no one could see how the oil industry was going to meet the demand for gaso-

line. Senator LaFollette * had predicted that gasoline would
go to one dollar per gallon and a good many sensible people
feared that he was right. The Badische process by which the
entire barrel of crude oil could, if necessary, be converted into
gasoline was therefore of the utmost potential value.

But fundamentally more important, perhaps, was a second
consideration—the conversion of coal into oil. Throughout
the history of the oil industry there have been recurrent crises
when it seemed that crude oil reserves were dwindling dangerously. The nation was experiencing, at that time, such a crisis.
New fields which had been brought in were disappointing in
size, and in the United States there was a widespread pessi-
mism about oil prospects. Mexican fields had shown some
promise, but the most abundant supplies were of poor quality,
containing as little as two or three per cent of gasoline. The
least hopeful of the American authorities estimated the total
known reserves of oil in the United States as not more than
seven years' supply.†

While not so pessimistic as that, most of the people in
Standard's organization considered it prudent to explore alternative sources of liquid fuel. Accordingly, some costly programs had been undertaken. The first was to prospect for and
acquire good deposits of oil shale; and the second, to try to
develop economical processes of roasting this shale to extract
the oil. Standard had gone far enough along both lines to be
somewhat discouraged. The good shale deposits of large size
were in Colorado, Wyoming and Utah, one to two thousand
miles from large consuming oil markets. To mine the shale
and transport it to a location suitable for roasting or retorting
was a colossal undertaking. Retorting of shale had been carried on in Scotland over several generations; the process was
entirely workable, but costs of equipment and operation were
high. Last of all, the shale oil when obtained—an average ex-

---

* The elder.
† See report of Federal Oil Conservation Board 1926.

pected yield was about one barrel from each ton of shale—presented more problems in refining than our lowest grades of crude oil.

By contrast, the Badische method of hydrogenating coal seemed much more rational and attractive. This method converted the coal directly into an oil product containing a reasonable proportion of gasoline, and by treating again with hydrogen, could convert the entire balance, if necessary, to gasoline. It was known that America had enough coal deposits of fair quality and in locations near consuming areas to provide for its oil requirements for hundreds of years at least.

It was 1926 when this small group of Standard Oil Company (N.J.) executives sat there in Heidelberg and talked of the future of the oil industry. It seemed clear that the German hydrogenation processes, and the new horizons they opened, were tremendously significant—perhaps more significant than any technical factor ever introduced into the oil industry up to this time. Their commercial importance would depend, of course, upon the cost of equipment and operations involved. The basic scientific problems seemed to be mostly solved, but the economic result would depend upon the effort spent in developing and improving the practical operations.

It was clear also that these new techniques affected another factor in the world's oil picture, that is, the nationalistic factor. Every nation had to have oil. If nature had not put oil within a country's borders, it had to be imported. Save for the United States and Russia, the nations which were the great oil consumers were not important oil producers. But Europe and even Asia, Africa and the west coast of South America had large coal supplies. Although hydrogenation of coal probably could never compete on an economic basis with crude oil, so long as supplies of the latter were adequate for world demand, it could be made the foundation of a protected manufacturing industry in many countries willing to pay the price.

By this time another officer of the company had joined the party at Heidelberg. It was agreed we must at once determine as well as we could the present status and prospects of the hydrogenation technique.

In the following days all our party inspected the laboratories and plants at Ludwigshafen. We talked separately and in groups with the Badische executives. The best guess we could make was that, although it would probably be several years before the hydrogenation operations would be ready for general use, it was very likely that they would eventually prove to be practical on a large scale. The cost of gasoline produced from coal would, we guessed, be from 15 to 30 cents per gallon,* much higher than that of gasoline from crude oil so long as new reserves of oil could be found, but not high enough to prevent the growth of the automobile industry if oil supplies should fail. And although there were very little data yet available, it seemed also probable that the hydrogenation process would also be of value in the refining of natural petroleum.

We considered whether we should try to buy world rights under the process, and decided very quickly against this approach. The Badische had obviously spent many millions already on it. And they were so sure of its great potential value that only a very large offer could appeal to them. But from our standpoint it was clearly impossible to offer a great sum for a process which was still in the early stages of development and which was based on catalytic chemistry entirely outside our range of experience.

The only feasible approach for any immediate trade seemed to be to offer our cooperation and financial help in developing and perfecting the process and ask for a part interest in return for our future efforts and expenditures. We sat down at our hotel one evening and drafted a tentative proposal along these

* This guess proved about right. Some estimates as low as 11 cents were made later but actual experience was nearer 25 cents.

lines which was to be subject, of course, to the approval of Standard's Board of Directors in New York.

The next morning we met the full board of the Badische company and presented our suggestions. Their reaction was favorable in principle.

There followed a discussion of the problem as they saw it. A first consideration was their company position. The Badische company had been for many years a member of a trade association made up of companies in the dye industry and related chemical manufacture in Germany. The association was called the "Interessen Gemeinshaft Farbenindustrie," translatable as "Community of Interest of the Dye Industry." It had started as a trade association but had been developing toward more and more unified operations, and the decision had been reached to merge the six other companies making up the association with the Badische company to form a single corporate unit known as "I.G. Farbenindustrie, A.G.," the initials "A.G." standing for "Aktiengesellschaft," or a "share-company." The other members of the new combination were all familiar with the work of Badische on hydrogenation, and it was impossible for the Badische group alone to make any commitment.

Beyond this internal question there were other considerations. The Badische company had already acquired extensive deposits of lignite, or brown coal, in the Leipzig-Halle area and believed it had the cheapest coal in Germany suitable for hydrogenation. Nevertheless the new industry would still need government protection of some kind. Would there be more difficulty in getting this protection if they dealt with us?

Last of all, there was the matter of technical cooperation between the Badische organization and Standard's. On each side technical knowledge and experience in its own industry, laboriously acquired over the years and added to day by day, was one of the most valuable assets.

CHAPTER III

AMERICAN RIGHTS IN GERMAN SYNTHETIC RUBBER

During the summer of 1926 the question of how to establish some sort of working arrangement on the hydrogenation process continued to receive the attention of Standard Oil Company (N.J.) and the Badische Company. In the late summer the Germans came to New York. The merger of the Badische organization into the new German chemical combine, I. G. Farbenindustrie, was now completely effective, and Dr. Carl Bosch, chairman of the Badische, had taken up his duties as chairman of the merged companies. He certainly favored an agreement of some kind with Standard. But it seemed to us that the Germans overestimated the immediate commercial value of the oil-from-coal processes because they had no real conception of the magnitude of the American oil industry and no appreciation of the economy of human labor in oil production by existing methods. I made an estimate for them at the time which showed that the total direct labor involved in producing and refining a bucket of crude oil was about the same as a farmer expended in drawing a bucket of water from his own well in the barnyard. How could any chemical synthesis compete with this?

Mr. Teagle decided that the best way to show the Germans what the oil industry really was would be to take Dr. Bosch on one of the regular inspection tours which Standard's president made twice a year. Our routine was to spend the day motoring, visiting oil and gas fields, pumping stations, and refineries, rejoining the inspection car in the evening for conferences with the field men and an overnight ride to the next center of operations. Three weeks of this, with an occasional day of rest, covered the oil centers and the principal cities from New York to San Francisco and left with Dr. Bosch an impression not only of the oil industry but also of the vast potential strength of America, which remained with him throughout his life.

After our return to New York negotiations moved satisfactorily. By November it was generally accepted that in some way the two companies should cooperate in developing the hydrogenation technique. Pending the completion of actual terms of agreement, the parties were to begin exchanging views and some technical information directly bearing on the process. Standard thereupon undertook an active development program in the newest and most difficult field of chemical effort: high pressure catalytic hydrogenation. To carry out this program we needed an entirely new technical center and the ablest staff that could be recruited to man it.

In the organization of the industrial research program for the company, beginning in 1919, I had relied upon three old friends as our principal advisors. These men were Dr. Ira Remsen, president emeritus of Johns Hopkins University and the leading organic chemist of his time; Dr. Robert A. Millikan, physicist and later Nobel prize winner, who was head of the California Institute of Technology; and Dr. Warren K. Lewis, head of the department of chemical engineering of the Massachusetts Institute of Technology. Standard's contribution to the hydrogenation process, we were convinced, would lie mainly in the field of chemical engineering. It was therefore agreed that we should take the problem to Dr. Lewis.

After the most careful analysis we decided to start a large new development laboratory at our Baton Rouge, Louisiana, refinery. Our thought was that in creating a new technical center here we would not only benefit by the natural advantages

of this Gulf Coast region, already on its way to becoming
the oil center of the country, but also revitalize the local organization by this infusion of new technical brains and thus
fit it to carry forward on an industrial basis any new developments which come out of the scientific work. Seldom has any
decision of American industry proved more fortunate.

To organize the new laboratory Dr. Lewis reommended
one of his associates, Professor Robert T. Haslam. Professor
Haslam obtained a leave of absence from the Institute for a
few months in the spring of 1927, intending to return to his
post in the autumn. But before his leave expired he found,
as several of us had before him, that one cannot easily turn
away and leave unfinished the tasks which a great industry
lays before those who once assume its responsibilities. He remained to carry on the work he had started.*

The staff of the new laboratory which Professor Haslam
organized was headed by Robert P. Russell, assistant professor
of chemical engineering at M.I.T.† and consisted largely of
junior members of the M.I.T. faculty and of its affiliated
School of Chemical Engineering Practice. It was this group
of young chemical engineers which carried, almost alone for
some years, the burden of development of the processes
acquired by Standard from the Germans.

In the early summer of 1927, a party of Standard officials,
including Mr. Haslam and Mr. William C. Asbury of his new
Baton Rouge staff, went to Germany for detailed talks with
the I.G. scientists. By this time the Germans were becoming
quite frank in their disclosures of technical information. It
was understood on both sides that some agreement which
would permit technical cooperation was certain to be made,
although no one could yet predict what it would be.

In the autumn of 1927 Dr. August von Knieriem, the Ba-

---

* Mr. Haslam eventually became an officer and director of Standard Oil
Co. (N.J.).

† Mr. Russell succeeded the author when he retired as President of
Standard Oil Development Company in 1944.

dische legal director, came to New York. Together he and I made an outline draft of the first contract between Standard and I.G. Everyone realized the potential importance of the agreement, and our negotiator's draft was subjected to the most careful study by the lawyers for each party. Mr. John W. Davis, former Solicitor General of the United States,* represented Standard as its general legal counsel and Mr. Charles Neave, former President of the International General Electric Company was patent counsel. The senior officers and directors of both companies followed the negotiations closely and the final contracts were promptly accepted and signed in September, 1927, on the authorization of the Boards of Directors of the parties.

Fundamentally the arrangement was much like that proposed by Standard in Ludwigshafen in April of the preceding year but was limited entirely to the United States. All the subsequent investigations had confirmed the reasoning of the original plan. Under the circumstances, the best road for any immediate trade was to arrange for cooperation and let Standard's future expenditures in developing the process buy an interest while it was acquiring experience in the new catalytic techniques and building up an American organization competent to perfect and use the processes.

Under the 1927 agreement, therefore, Standard made no cash payment to the I.G., but undertook to cooperate technically in the development of oil hydrogenation in the United States only and to this end to erect and operate as soon as possible a plant having a capacity of 40,000 tons of hydrogenated oil products per year. The research and development expenditure which this would require was recognized as being very high—to be measured in millions of dollars. Standard was to have the right to use the process in the United States for commercial plants aside from this development plant,

---

* Ambassador to England 1918-1922. Democratic candidate for President of the United States in 1924.

upon payment of a fair royalty. I.G. was to keep all its United States patents and control the licensing of the process to other parties, but in compensation for its costs in the development work Standard was to be paid one-half of all royalties collected by I.G. under their patents. As a further consideration, and also to avoid conflict of financial interest with its own oil refining developments, Standard was to pay to I.G. one-half the royalties it collected from the licensing in the United States by Standard of its related oil refining improvements, although Standard was to remain in full control of such licensing.

The contract therefore dealt, not with any tangible property, but entirely with new processes, technical information and royalties under patent licenses, a type of intangible property right especially subject to legal uncertainties and technicalities. Germany was just recovering from the economic chaos of an inflation which had made most property rights based on contract or debt valueless. The federal regime was in the hands of the well intentioned but weak Weimar Republic controlled by the Social Democrats. There was a large and aggressive communist minority in the industrial provinces and strong territorial regimes with royalist and separatist tendencies in the Rhineland and Bavaria. No one could forecast the political or economic future of Germany.

The contract with Standard was to run for twenty-five years. At the request of the Germans, it was supplemented by an exchange of letters between the two companies, signed by Mr. Teagle for Standard and Dr. Bosch for I.G. These letters expressed the reliance of each upon the good faith of the other and declared that the parties would renegotiate the contract provisions to meet future legal problems as they arose. The text of the two letters, which were identical, read:

"Referring to our agreement of Sept. 27, 1927, we wish to state that it is our understanding that the discussions of the parties in connection with the negotiation of this agreement have shown that each party purposes to hold itself willing to take care of any future eventualities in the spirit of mutual helpfulness, particularly along the following lines:

In the event the performance of the agreement or of any material provision thereof by either party should be hereafter restrained or prevented by operation of any existing or future law, or the beneficial interest of either party be alienated to a substantial degree by operation of law or governmental authority, the parties should enter into new negotiations in the spirit of the present contract and endeavor to adapt their relations to the changed conditions which have so arisen.

Further, in the event the interest of either party should suffer from some cause which might be rectified by the change of the form of the agreement, while preserving its substance and the interest and obligations of the parties in the subject matter thereof, the parties should, and will, endeavor to revise the form of the agreement in such particulars as may be necessary to overcome the difficulty encountered.

This letter is intended to make a record of the discussions of the foregoing subjects and of the understanding which we have of the position and intentions of the parties and of the spirit in which the parties have agreed they will approach and endeavor to carry thru the readjustment of their contractual relations if such readjustment is necessary for the protection of the interests of one party and does not diminish the effective rights or interests of the other party, as fixed by the original contract."

By American legal standards these letters were only an unnecessary record of good intentions.* But no one could object to their purpose, and with their own past experience and uncertain future in mind, the Germans thought it a good thing to supplement the actual contract covering the long uncharted course ahead by these letters express-

---

* Under the mistaken impression that these letters had originated two years later when the 1927 contract was replaced by three new agreements, the letters were described by critics of Standard appearing before a Congressional Committee in 1942 as a "Co-ordination Agreement" to "co-ordinate" the three 1929 contracts.

ing the moral obligation of the two companies to try to correct
any inequities which might arise.

The 1927 contract was too limited in its scope to be entirely
satisfactory to either side, even when it was made, and the
difficulties quickly became more apparent. Having no basis
of agreement at all outside of the United States, the two companies found themselves competing to obtain foreign patents
on inventions on which they were supposed to be working
together. The inventions and improvements useful in oil hydrogenation could usually be applied also in coal hydrogenation but the fate of coal hydrogenation in the United States
still remained entirely in the hands of the I.G.; and neither
Standard nor any other American company could do anything about the process in the United States without the consent of the Germans. It was also becoming quite apparent that
the technical knowledge exchanged between the parties and
acquired by both as the result of their joint research on oil
hydrogenation was of great potential value outside the scope
of the contract. Each party would inevitably use to its own
best advantage, everywhere and in every way, whatever it
learned from the other. Frank and full cooperation in research under such conditions was an impossibility.

Through the next two years, while we were proceeding together as best we could with the oil hydrogenation research
in the United States only, the parties discussed these difficulties and new questions amicably. There was an effort on both
sides to apply in the broadest way the principles of fair dealing to which the chief executives of the two companies had
committed them by their exchange of letters in 1927.

Standard was quite willing to expand its existing limited
interest in the German hydrogenation processes, an interest for which it had made no direct payment, but the Germans could not see that this would be either practical or
fair to them. Dr. Bosch pointed out the possible conflicts of
interest between the I.G. and Standard in the upbuilding of a

great synthetic oil industry in Europe, and was also quite frank in saying that his company had now spent such enormous sums on the hydrogenation process that they could not part with any further interest in it save for a very large direct payment. The only clear road Dr. Bosch could see was for Standard to buy all the I.G. interest in the process except for Germany.

This suggestion was referred by Standard's Board to a committee made up of Mr. Heinrich Riedemann, Standard's general European sales manager, Mr. Edgar M. Clark, vice president in charge of refineries, Mr. Haslam and myself. In December, 1928, the committee recommended a purchase formula. Standard would buy the hydrogenation process and all substitute and related processes of the I.G. for the world outside of Germany, but the purchase price would be reduced below the figure which it had been intimated was in the minds of the Germans by leaving with them a royalty interest. This would also give a continuing incentive for the Germans to help Standard improve the process and secure licensees. At least part of the purchase price was to be paid in Standard's stock, instead of in cash. This would give the Germans a further incentive to assist Standard in commercializing the process. Standard's Board approved this formula and it was transmitted about the end of the year 1928 to the Germans who were understood to have reacted favorably.

In March, 1929, the I.G. directors came to New York with the avowed intention of completing the discussions. They began by accepting in principle Standard's purchase offer. They preferred to have the entire purchase price instead of only a part of it in Standard stock. The amount was fixed at 546,011 shares, which was about 2 per cent of Standard's total issued stock. During the period of the discussions and before the actual delivery of the stock, its market price fluctuated through a considerable range and in the period immediately following the market price was as low as $20 a share

—as high as $80 a share. On this basis the purchase price might have been said to be anything between $11,000,000 and $44,000,000. The average market price on November 8, 1929, the day preceding the actual delivery of the shares, was $65 and on this basis the purchase could be said to have cost $35,-000,000 which was the figure used on Standard's books.

But while the Germans were willing to accept Standard's offer for the hydrogenation process, they pointed out the necessity of reaching agreement also on two other lines. First of all they wanted to finalize the long-drawn-out discussions which had been going on in Germany concerning the basis on which Standard's German subsidiary, D.A.P.G., would distribute for the I.G. the synthetic gasoline * which they were soon to be making from brown coal in large quantities. Standard had already accepted this in principle, and in due time these German gasoline sales discussions were concluded satisfactorily and reduced to a contract.

The last and most difficult question arose from the fear of the I.G. that Standard would use the knowledge of catalytic chemistry which it drew from them in the joint work on hydrogenation to compete with I.G. in its own chemical business. If, for example, I.G. showed Standard how to treat coal tars catalytically to make intermediate oils for further refining into gasoline, what was to prevent Standard from using this education to start the manufacture of dye intermediates from coal tar? The answer, of course, was that Standard was in the oil business, not the dye business, and would not jeopardize its technical cooperation with I.G., which was indispensable for the development of hydrogenation, for the sake of some small additional earnings to be made by entering a field so remote from any of its business as the dye industry. But further discussion of this subject showed that there might be border-line cases and that Standard as well as I.G. might have

* In excess of the outlet provided by the jointly owned distributing company Gasoline A.G.

cause for concern. A formal agreement called the Division of Fields Agreement * was therefore drafted under which the two companies declared their intention of adhering to their own respective lines of business—that is, the oil business for Standard and the chemical business for I.G. Each agreed to offer to sell to the other, on reasonable terms, any new development it might have which was really in the other's line of business. Although these provisions were limited to the period in which the parties were to be cooperating technically in the perfection of the hydrogenation process and seemed at the time to be fair and constructive, they were later criticized as tending, in theory at least, to discourage possible competition between two great industrial companies.

Whatever might be the theoretical objections, these two reciprocal covenants between Standard and I.G. were never invoked, and were of no practical importance. On the other hand, the Division of Fields Agreement contained a third covenant which became of great importance. Under the third covenant I.G. agreed to offer to Standard a minority participation in any new process I.G. developed for making chemical products from oil or natural gas. It was through this last covenant of the Division of Fields Agreement that there came to America the Buna synthetic rubber process by which synthetic rubber could be made from oil.

The main agreement for the purchase of the hydrogenation process became quite complicated before it was completed in November, 1929. To meet increasing complexities of the federal and state laws, Standard Oil Company (N.J.) had become a holding company and it was necessary for it to act in such matters only with its principal operating unit, a Delaware corporation called Standard Oil Company of New Jersey. It also became necessary to organize a new Delaware corporation to take title to and manage the hydrogenation patents, in

* Appendix, p. 249.

order to avoid conflicting obligations of Standard itself under some existing patent contracts. Standard made a virtue of this last formal necessity by inviting I.G. to subscribe to 20 per cent of the capital stock of the patent management company. This brought the Germans into direct contact with the actual licensing of the patents, so that they could be of all possible assistance and also could be assured that the licensing was always handled in the fairest way, not favoring Standard's own subsidiaries at the expense of I.G., who were by the purchase contract entitled to continuing royalties to be paid out of what was collected by the patent management company.

It was well known throughout the world that the hydrogenation process had originated with the I.G. and its predecessors, the Badische, and that their laboratories were the seat of most of the world's knowledge of this new and difficult branch of chemistry. To capitalize on this reputation Standard therefore called its new patent management company, which was responsible for selling the German processes to the oil industry of the world, Standard-I.G. Company. On their own part, the Germans were very willing to agree to these plans. Pride in their scientific achievements was always very strong with them and any commercial arrangement which gave them full credit before the world for their technical genius was more than welcome. Our recognition of this national characteristic was perhaps the most important factor in maintaining a steady flow of scientific information from the great I.G. laboratories through the years which followed.

The 1929 agreement was widely publicized at the time both in the United States and in Germany. The statement issued by the Standard Oil Company (N.J.) in November, 1929 read:

1—The patents relating to hydrogenation of coal and oil of I. G. Farbenindustrie and Standard Oil Company (N. J.) for the world outside of Germany will be taken over by a corporation which will be owned jointly by the parties. Standard will assume the management of this corporation.

2—A marketing outlet for the production of synthetic gasoline by the I. G. Farbenindustrie in Germany is provided on terms which safeguard the interests of the I. G. Farbenindustrie.

3—The existing close cooperation between the parties in research and development on new products and processes of mutual interest is enlarged and perpetuated.

The New York *Times* of December 2, 1929, gave a more complete picture of the final arrangements under which the German Hydrogenation Process came to the United States. The *Times'* story read as follows:

PLAN WIDER RIGHTS FOR OIL CONVERSION

Standard of New Jersey and German Dye
Trust to License Other Companies

HOPE TO AID THE INDUSTRY

F. A. Howard Named President of Corporation
Formed to Push Hydrogenation Process

Patents of the German Dye Trust covering the hydrogenation process of extracting gasoline from coal and changing heavy crude petroleum to the more valuable lighter oils will not be held exclusively by the Standard Oil Company of New Jersey in the United States, but will be offered for license as soon as practical, according to an announcement made in The Lamp, official publication of the Standard Oil Company of New Jersey.

The Standard Oil Company of New Jersey is now building three commercial plants for the utilization of the process on low grades of crude oil, and the I. G. Farbenindustrie Aktiengesellschaft, with which the American company has an arrangement for the use of the process outside of Germany, has a plant operating in Germany for the extraction of gasoline from coal and low grade oils.

The company, which will handle the patents for the world outside of Germany, was recently formed. The

Lamp's announcement discloses that it will be called the Standard-I. G. Company. The Standard Oil Company of New Jersey owns the majority of the stock in the new corporation and will assume responsibility for its management. The technical work in the United States on the development of the process and the construction of plants will remain for the present in the hands of the Standard Oil Development Company, a technical subsidiary of the Standard Oil Company of New Jersey, which has been developing the process since the initial arrangement was made with I. G. Farbenindustrie about two years ago.

The Lamp article announces that the following will be directors of the Standard-I. G. Company: E. M. Clark, Walter Duisberg, R. T. Haslam, F. A. Howard, Peter Hurll, H. A. Riedemann, H. G. Seidel, A. A. Straw, Otto von Schrenk and Guy Wellman. The officers will be F. A. Howard, president; E. M. Clark, vice president; M. H. Eames, secretary, and R. P. Resor, treasurer. This company will handle all business aspects of the joint development of the process by the Standard Oil Development Company and the I. G. Farbenindustrie.

In announcing the plans for the licensing of other companies for the use of the process, The Lamp says:

"It has never been the plan to restrict the use of the process to the subsidiary and affiliated units of the Standard Oil Company (N. J.). The views of the I. G. Farbenindustrie A. G. and this company are, and have been, that the process will have the best chance of exerting a maximum constructive influence on the oil industry if it is offered for license in the United States at the earliest practicable time and on a basis which will provide opportunity for cooperation of the industry at large in its further development."

The formation of the new company is stated to be the first step in the program for the licensing of other companies for the use of the process, which is described as "a definite although not an easy solution" of the problem which is now facing the petroleum industry of disposing of the ever-increasing production of heavy fuel oil beyond the natural demand for it.

Following completion of the 1929 contracts, Standard had unrestricted access to the scientific work relating to coal and oil under way in Germany. Research on hydrogenation processes were being pushed on a scale unprecedented in the brief annals of organized industrial research. At three great factories, Ludwigshafen on the Rhine, at a new plant called Oppau also on the Rhine just below Ludwigshafen, and at the enormous Leuna synthetic ammonia plant near Leipzig, hundreds of German engineers and chemists were at work on plans for the new German synthetic oil industry. Standard's young technical organization in Louisiana was being expanded but found it difficult to digest the mass of costly research data from the I.G. laboratories and technical reports from our own engineers inspecting the German experimental installations.

Included in the reports from I.G.'s laboratories were references to current research work on two new synthetic processes, the production of fatty acids from paraffin wax and the manufacture of rubber from hydrocarbon gases similar to those from oil or natural gas. These new synthetic processes did not come within the terms of Standard's purchase contract, which was limited to petroleum products and substitutes for them. But under the Division of Fields Agreement which had been intended to prevent the two companies from becoming irritated over minor conflicts between the chemical and oil fields, I.G. had agreed to offer Standard on reasonable terms a minority interest in any new process which used oil or natural gas as raw material for a chemical manufacturing operation. The embryo processes for synthetic fatty acid and synthetic rubber seemed to fall within this language and the question of procedure on such matters was raised with I.G. After a short negotiation the question was settled to the satisfaction of both companies by a new formula which von Knieriem of I.G. and I evolved out of the advice of our associates.

Instead of paying the I.G. in cash for a minority share in processes of this kind in which Standard was interested, we would pay by giving them a minority share in any similar processes of our own. This new formula was incorporated in a contract of September 30, 1930,* under which the parties organized a Joint American Study Company to handle these embryo oil-chemical processes.

* Appendix, p. 252.

CHAPTER IV

INFANCY OF SYNTHETIC RUBBER

The Joint American Study Company (abbreviated to "Jasco") which was to be the joint vehicle for the commercial testing and licensing of new processes developed by either party for making chemical products from oil raw materials was organized as a Louisiana corporation on October 23, 1930. Standard and I.G. owned the shares of the company equally, financed it equally, and alternated the presidency between them. When a new process for creating chemical products from oil raw materials had been developed to the point where it was ready for commercial testing and licensing, the originator was to offer the process to the joint company for that purpose. Each new process was to be a separate venture of the joint company. The party originating each process was entitled to a 62½ per cent interest (five-eighths) and the other party 37½ per cent (three-eighths).

At the time the Joint American Study Company was formed, I.G. had a group of new processes ready to deliver to it. It was ten years later before Standard had originated any process to which the provisions of the agreement could be applicable. This process, the production of the Butyl type of synthetic rubber, was an indirect result of research by Standard on an earlier process brought into the Joint Study Company by the I.G.

One of the Buna rubber processes was the first thing to be taken up by Jasco. The name "Buna," given by the I.G. to their type of synthetic rubber, comes from the initial syllables of the two materials first used to make it: butadiene and natrium (sodium). After methodical exploration of possible origins for synthetic rubber, beginning with the "methyl rubber" which they had made in the first World War, I.G. had chosen as their starting point *butadiene*, probably the simplest structurally of all molecules which will readily join hands to form long chains. Three problems had still to be solved before Buna could be successful: it was not yet known how to produce large quantities of butadiene cheaply; the polymerization or conversion operation—for which the Germans at first used metallic sodium as a catalyst—was expensive and troublesome; and the Buna product itself was inferior in quality.

In their work up to this time the I.G. had produced butadiene from acetylene gas, which they obtained in the usual way from calcium carbide made from coal and limestone in an electric furnace. Since it was not being made from oil or natural gas, Buna rubber did not come, at that stage of its development, within the terms of the Joint Study agreement. However, I.G. was working on a process for making acetylene from oil gas or natural gas by passing the gases through an electric arc. If butadiene could be produced from oil in this or any other way, its conversion into Buna rubber would automatically go to the Joint Study Company for development.

It was decided that Standard, through the Joint Study Company, would undertake to develop at Baton Rouge the conversion of oil and natural gas into acetylene gas, and that the I.G. would continue in their German laboratories their work on the production of Buna rubber from acetylene derived from coal.

The electric arc process had already been operated on a laboratory scale in Germany. The next step was to have apparatus built and tested to determine whether the operation would work well on a large scale, what kinds of oil gases or natural gas would work best, and what the costs would be.

If we succeeded in making acetylene out of oil and natural gas—the first step in making butadiene—the parties faced another practical difficulty. Acetylene gas is very active chemically. It cannot be stored conveniently in any great quantity because of the hazard of explosion and the cost of storage tanks. I.G. suggested that this difficulty might be overcome by two additional steps—first converting our acetylene into acetaldehyde and then converting the acetaldehyde into acetic acid. Conversion to acetaldehyde was, in any case, the first step in the manufacture of butadiene from acetylene. There was no market for the acetaldehyde we might make in our process experiments, but acetic acid was a normal chemical product which Standard was then buying in small quantities for use in a petroleum alcohol plant.

The experimental electric arc acetylene plant at Baton Rouge was put into operation in September, 1932. By the end of 1935 most of the technical problems had been worked out. It was clear, however, that the cost of producing butadiene by this method would be too high to permit synthetic rubber made from it to compete with natural rubber. Nor did the parties have much success in trying to recoup the experimental expense through the sale of acetic acid. There were difficulties with the process of conversion, and the supply was irregular, so that it was hard to make any favorable sales contracts for it. The experimental work had cost $1,600,000 in excess of credits for the acetic acid sold. I.G. and Standard shared this expense equally.

In the meantime the I.G. efforts to develop the Buna polymerization process had progressed steadily from a scientific standpoint. But, like the experimentation in making butadiene at Baton Rouge, results seemed always to fall just short of being commercially valuable. I.G. had abandoned the sodium polymerization process because even the lowest costs were too high and the best products were not good enough. They had switched over their main efforts to a method called "emulsion polymerization" in which the butadiene was agitated in warm water containing soap or other emulsifying agents. This proc-

ess dispersed the butadiene in fine droplets throughout the
water, making a sort of milk. When first describing this
process, I.G. told us somewhat ruefully that a plant to produce any great amount of synthetic rubber would have to
consist of acres of huge tanks, with emulsions sitting around
in them polymerizing slowly. One possible cure for this difficulty was to find a new catalyst, and the search proved arduous. Polymerization time was at first measured in weeks, then
days, and after years of work, in hours. Product quality,
however, was still bad. To improve the quality, I.G. undertook an exhaustive investigation of the possibility of introducing other molecules into the butadiene chain. It was a
course which followed many ups and downs, but out of it,
finally, came the Buna products on which the synthetic rubber industry was mainly built.

It was soon recognized that the production of a synthetic
rubber is one thing, but its practical fabrication into marketable products is another. To determine the best methods for
handling the synthetic product and its quality in the finished
goods was obviously the work of a rubber manufacturing
company. Negotiations were therefore begun by the Joint
Company in 1932 with The B. F. Goodrich Company, one of
the largest and oldest of the American rubber goods manufacturers. The purpose was to arrive at some sort of an arrangement under which Goodrich would test the Buna products as
the I.G. produced them and report on their probable value
and uses.

During the year several drafts of proposed contracts were
exchanged between the parties. It was contemplated that I.G.
would not only furnish the necessary large samples of Buna
rubber, but also would supply a technical expert from Germany, who would bring with him all the German experience
in the compounding and vulcanizing of the Buna. The original idea of the arrangement was very simple, and both parties
thought they had come to an agreement; but before all the

lawyers for the two sides had finished protecting their clients, it became so complicated and difficult that the principals despaired of reaching a satisfactory conclusion. They tried to back-track and arrive at some simple agreement which would avoid the disputed details in connection with the handling of patents, but this also ran into a dead-end street.

The Joint American Study Company then opened discussions with the General Tire and Rubber Company of Akron. By the end of May, 1933, an agreement had been reached and shipment of samples to the Akron factory had been begun. Dr. Stoecklin of I.G. spent some months in the United States working at the General laboratories and visiting other rubber experts. At this same time the Goodyear Tire and Rubber Company became interested but it was decided to await the outcome of the work with General before doing anything further. General's final report on the study was dated April 27, 1934. It found the Buna product unsuitable for handling in standard factory equipment, and the quality of the products made from it definitely inferior to those made of natural rubber.

This report was, for us in America, the "end of the beginning" of the Buna development. Still working on the electric arc process and its related developments, the Joint Study Company had found a workable, but much too expensive process for obtaining butadiene from oil or natural gas. All along the line, we had attained a fair degree of technical success, but commercially our efforts seemed to have ended in complete failure.

I.G. seemed to have arrived at about the same impasse in their work in Germany. They were able to convert butadiene into a synthetic rubber which appeared superficially to be of fairly good quality—even better than natural rubber in some few characteristics. But the production cost was still far out of the range of commercial competition with natural rubber, and the quality was found, both in the German and in the American experiments, to be not only inferior on the whole but also unsuitable for commercial handling in rubber factory equipment. It was doubtful if any quantity of the Buna could be sold at any price so long as natural rubber was available.

Just at this time another element was introduced into the situation abroad by the German government's "Four Year Plan." Under this program, adopted in 1933 by the new National Socialist government, the German economy was to be rebuilt within four years under the leadership of Hermann Goering to achieve the maximum degree of national self-sufficiency. The synthetic oil-from-coal program, already well started, was to be greatly expanded and real efforts made to develop other new synthetic industries.

Because of its importance both from a military and economic standpoint, synthetic rubber was to be one of the pillars of this autarchy program. Germany had been experiencing chronic and increasing difficulties in trying to make a solvent foreign trade balance sheet. Footing the annual bill for crude rubber imports was one of the worst foreign exchange problems. So the production of synthetic rubber became a part of the German autarchy program, with the government paying the costs and directing the procedure. Experimental production of Buna was continued and increased. Small quantities were soon being delivered to the entire German rubber industry, which had to use them as best they could. These products were sold by I.G. under government direction, the German rubber fabricators being compelled to absorb established quotas. The entire world knew of this situation, and the great American rubber companies, all of whom maintained contacts with the German rubber trade, followed developments there with mixed feelings. While there was general interest in the scientific aspects of the German synthetic rubber program, no one here envied the German rubber companies who were compelled to absorb the inferior Buna product.

During the time that the German Buna was passing through

its "children's diseases," there had been two American synthetic rubber developments. These were "Thiokol" and "neoprene," and both were beautiful examples of Midgley's theories.

There is no chemical relation between the composition of Thiokol and that of natural rubber, or any of the rubber-like substances previously synthesized. It was made by chemically reacting ethylene dichloride with sodium polysulfide. Neoprene has some resemblance to the isoprene molecule of natural rubber, but apparently the essential point in both cases was that the basic chemical units had hands extended ready to join into long coiled chains like the rubber molecule.

The discovery of Thiokol was accidental. In 1922, Dr. J. C. Patrick, a Kansas City chemist, while trying to find a product suitable as an automobile radiator anti-freeze, mixed ethylene dichloride and sodium polysulfide. To his surprise, a milky suspension was formed, which, upon coagulation, had marked rubber-like properties. It did not need the addition of sulphur to cross-stitch the chains together. On heating, it would cross-stitch itself and turn into a product resembling vulcanized natural rubber. Its raw materials were easy to make and the process itself was not difficult. Thiokol could be made in a variety of grades. Small commercial production was begun eight years later in 1930. It was sold at a price of 30 cents per pound in competition with natural rubber at 8 to 16 cents per pound. The volume of sales, as compared with natural rubber, was insignificant—only about 15 tons the first year and about 500 tons in 1935. This small amount went into a few special rubber compounds. The outstanding advantage of Thiokol over natural rubber was its resistance to oil, but its other peculiarities were such that even for this purpose its uses turned out to be limited.

Neoprene originated in the work of Father Nieuland, professor of chemistry at Notre Dame University. He reported to the American Chemical Society in 1925 a method to control the polymerization of two molecules of acetylene to form the hydrocarbon molecule called *vinyl acetylene*. The du Pont Company recognized the importance of Father Nieuland's work and took the exclusive rights to the discovery. In 1929 Wallace Caruthers and his du Pont associates found that vinyl acetylene could be reacted with hydrochloric acid to produce chloroprene, which displayed the ability to join hands with its neighbors to form long chains. The resulting product had rubber-like properties. The du Pont Company first called it "Duprene" and later "neoprene." By patient and aggressive research and development work they succeeded in commercializing this new product. By April, 1933, they were able to announce that their chloroprene plant was producing 2 tons per month and would be brought to a capacity of 10 tons per month as quickly as possible.

The raw materials for neoprene were acetylene and chlorine. The production process was difficult, and some stages involved an exceptionally bad explosion hazard. Like Thiokol, neoprene was highly resistant to petroleum oils, but its other properties were in the main more satisfactory to the rubber trade. From a small beginning the commercial business expanded slowly but continuously. By the early part of 1935 production was at the rate of 200 tons per year. The market price was then $1.00 per pound. The price of natural rubber in 1935 was 11 to 14 cents a pound and the American consumption was just under 500,000 tons per year.

The German effort to produce a general utility rubber, to be used as a substitute for natural rubber, as distinguished from a new product for limited special purposes such as Thiokol or neoprene, had in the meantime been concentrated upon the "copolymer" form of Buna known as Buna-S for which the first U.S. patents were issued in 1933.* The inventors were Eduard Tschunkur and Walter Bock of the I. G. Leverkrusen works. It was made by introducing about 25 per cent of styrene into the butadiene chain. Styrene is a well-known

* Patents # 1,938,730–31.

chemical product which can be made from benzol and alcohol.

Dr. Fritz ter Meer, the I.G. director in charge of the Buna development, visited New York during the latter part of 1935 to confer with us about it. Like most of the high executives of the I.G., he was a scientist by training and was familiar with the research work as well as the commercial operations. At that time the production of Buna-S in Germany was 25 tons a month. By instruction from Goering's Economic Ministry it was supposed to reach 200 tons a month within one year, and 1000 tons a month (about 15 per cent of Germany's needs) in three years. The output was to be sold under government direction.

Dr. ter Meer's report on Buna-S at that time was far from encouraging. In its natural form the product was said to have some superior qualities, especially for tire treads, since in some but not all tests it seemed to show more resistance to wear than the best natural rubber. But it was still impossible to handle the Buna-S satisfactorily on the milling and compounding machines made for natural rubber. It could be handled on the regular machinery by adding a softening agent, but its good qualities were then lost. Moreover, the cost figures showed the product to be entirely hopeless from an economic standpoint; it could not compete in price with natural rubber.

Ter Meer had come to the conclusion that for immediate purposes neoprene might be more promising than Buna. Both in the United States and Germany a few experimental tires had been made of neoprene, and ter Meer thought at that time that a 100 per cent neoprene tire would prove better than a 100 per cent Buna tire. Neoprene could certainly be used much more readily in the existing equipment of the rubber industry than could Buna. As to raw materials, neoprene started with acetylene, upon which Buna was then also based in Germany, but neoprene required in addition only chlorine, which was cheaper and more abundant than styrene. So convinced were the I.G. people at this time of neoprene's superior promise, that they contemplated negotiating for the rights to make neoprene in Germany. They then proposed to discuss with the German government the possible substitution of neoprene for part or all of the projected 1000 ton per-month development of Buna.

Ter Meer's subsequent investigations here and in Germany made him abandon this plan. He later reported that it was another instance of the grass in the neighbor's field looking greener than one's own. The troubles with Buna had been quite obvious to him, but he had not been able to see the neoprene troubles until he looked more closely.*

Three years later, in the spring of 1938, the German government-subsidized production of Buna was far behind the original schedule, but had reached 5000 tons a year. This meant that German rubber manufacturers were required to absorb quotas of the unwanted product equal to perhaps 7 per cent of their total rubber consumption. Their complaints were continuous and bitter. Chief among their charges was that it took two to three times as much milling capacity to handle the Buna.

The only bright spot that had developed in the picture was the continued improvement of a variety of Buna known as "Buna-N," or "Perbunan" which had been invented by Tschunkur and another I.G. chemist, Erich Konrad, and patented in the United States in 1934.† This new rubber was made by combining butadiene with a substantial proportion of a rather expensive synthetic chemical known as "*acryloni-*

---

* In 1939 when Standard took over I.G.'s interest in Buna in the United States, it developed that in the course of its neoprene discussions with du Pont I.G. had promised du Pont that it would give them a chance to make a proposal before making any final decision on Buna in the United States. Standard had to make good on this promise but nothing ever came of it. Du Pont first stated it would be interested in Buna only on the basis of an exclusive license. We could not consider this. Later du Pont made an inquiry about terms for a possible non-exclusive license but no active negotiations were ever undertaken.

† Patent # 1,973,000.

trile." The especially valuable quality of Buna-N was its high resistance to attack by oil. Natural rubber, if exposed to contact with mineral oils, has a tendency to swell up, soften and finally to disintegrate—no matter how it is compounded and vulcanized. If oil hoses and gaskets for oil pipe lines are made of natural rubber, their life is apt to be short. This characteristic of natural rubber had always troubled rubber fabricators in Germany as well as elsewhere. Thiokol and neoprene met the difficulty, but each had its own objectionable peculiarities also. Buna-N was a definite advance in this special field.

Buna-N was introduced commercially in this country through an accident. Early in 1937 the du Pont neoprene plant was put out of commission for a lengthy period by an explosion. The rubber trade in America, now accustomed to using neoprene in small quantities for many special articles, found itself without supplies. The du Pont Company tried to do everything in its power to help these customers. Some of them were able to use Thiokol, but for many of them Thiokol was unsuitable. Du Pont brought this situation to the attention of I.G. and a small shipment of Buna-N was sent to the United States promptly. It was found to be entirely satisfactory to many of the American consumers who had been using neoprene and to new customers as well. The demand for Buna-N for special high-value uses increased steadily.

This demand, however, was infinitesimal compared with requirements for natural rubber at normal prices. The material did not replace rubber but went almost entirely into new uses where rubber had not been suitable. Total consumption reached a rate of about one ton a day. The selling price was from $1.00 to $1.20 a pound. At that time neoprene sold at 70 cents and natural rubber at 15 cents per pound.

Thus the German Buna was introduced into the American market in 1937. But its launching was far from being the event that Standard and I.G. had visualized years before. It did not replace natural rubber. It came, not as a new basic industry for the country, but as a high-priced speciality of very limited possibilities. It was not made, and apparently could not yet be made competitively, from oil or natural gas. It was produced in Germany from coal, and if any were to be made in America, the simplest course would be to make it in the same way, from coal-produced acetylene. Under these conditions it would have been technically outside our Joint Study contract and might have remained the sole property of I.G. Any report of synthetic rubber developments to this point would necessarily have concluded with the statement that there was as yet nothing in the whole picture of any great importance, either to the United States or to Standard Oil Company.

Meanwhile, however, besides the small commercial deliveries and samples of Buna-N which were coming into this country, some new samples of Buna-S were also being imported. The first general shipments of Buna-S samples to American rubber companies had begun in February, 1937. In September of that year, I.G. furnished Standard with a list of eight companies to whom they had sent several hundred pounds of samples. Arrangements for these samples had been made by these companies directly with I.G. The I.G.'s report to us of the interest displayed in the samples by these American rubber companies, the new interest in Buna-N, and inquiries concerning Buna we ourselves had received from some of the American companies, resulted in new discussions with I.G. in September, 1937. It was decided that the Joint Study Company would follow up the commercial market in the United States for Buna-N, the oil-resisting specialty rubber; and that there should be regular small importations of this type of Buna from Germany for the purpose. The importations were made by the I.G.'s regular sales agents in New York.

Then, in March, 1938, when the imported Buna-N was being received with increasing favor in the United States, I.G. reported to us that German manufacturers were having much better success in handling Buna-S, the tire rubber.

CHAPTER V

BUTYL RUBBER AND AVIATION GASOLINE

Unlike fiction, the factual record of any important scientific and economic development seems always to emerge as a tangled skein—never as a single, straight thread. This was certainly true of Buna rubber, which was paralleled through much of its course by other synthetic rubber developments. Perhaps the most important of these was Butyl rubber.

The story of Butyl started with a technical meeting at Ludwigshafen which I attended in April, 1932. Dr. Martin Müller-Cunradi, connected with the management of the Oppau works of the I.G. which adjoined Ludwigshafen, described a new scientific discovery which I.G. thought would interest us. He began by handing me a small glass jar half filled with a transparent viscous substance. It looked and felt like a heavy tar which by some miracle had been bleached and made as clear as water.

This product had been developed, he told me, at the Oppau laboratories. It was subsequently called by several trade names, the name most commonly used in the United States being "Vistanex."

The Vistanex was made from a well known by-product of oil refining called *iso-butylene*. Its molecule is like that of butadiene, save that it has only two free hands or chemical bonds with which to take hold of other molecules, whereas butadiene has four. Like butadiene, it is on the borderline between a gas and a liquid. If left in an open vessel at ordinary temperatures, it will evaporate and become a gas almost immediately, but if confined under slight pressure, or kept at a low temperature, it will remain liquid. It was well known that the isobutylene molecules were quite willing to join hands with one another, but generally they formed thin liquids similar to gasoline. In a few instances higher polymers similar to lubricating oils had been produced, but isobutylene had heretofore refused to link into longer chains.

Dr. Müller-Cunradi explained that his laboratory had recently discovered that if isobutylene was cooled to a temperature of approximately 100° F. below zero, and then treated with minute amounts of a little-known gas called *boron fluoride*, which served as a catalyst, the molecules would instantly combine into long chains. The result was a plastic solid. It was apparent that here was a possible method of making synthetic rubber. I examined the sample more closely. It was somewhat like rubber; at least it was slightly elastic. If it were a new starting point for rubber, it would be an important discovery, because, unlike butadiene, isobutylene was already available in the oil refining industry, and we had only to find means to recover and purify it.

Dr. Cunradi dispelled this dream by explaining that there were two difficulties. In the first place, although the Vistanex bore a slight resemblance to crude rubber, none that I.G. had yet been able to make was nearly elastic enough or strong enough to approach crude rubber in quality. The second difficulty was even more fundamental. The isobutylene molecule had only two free hands. When it was joined in chains, both hands were used, one on each end of each molecule, to link it to its neighbors. All the extended hands having been used to form the chain, the molecules were now smooth, and there was no way to take hold of them for cross-linking purposes. In other words, the isobutylene polymer could not be vulcanized. What, then, was the Vistanex good for?

One interesting characteristic was that, when heated to a high temperature, the long chains would break down again into the original molecules, and the solid Vistanex would revert to a gas, leaving nothing behind. A safety fuel for use in airplanes or in airships where the fire hazard was great could be carried in the form of Vistanex in solid masses which would be harmless under any condition. As fuel was needed, the Vistanex could be melted and decomposed into gas, which would operate the engines just as well as gasoline. It was an ideal safety fuel—as safe as coal, but like coal, it was hard to handle and although some experimental devices worked well, this plan to use Vistanex as a safe aviation fuel never materialized.

A more immediately practical use suggested for Vistanex was as a thickener for oils and greases. It was closely akin to lubricating oil in its chemical constitution. A minute percentage of Vistanex dissolved in the oil would produce an observable increase in viscosity without otherwise changing the oil, and this thickening effect could be used to convert a thin or "light" lubricating oil into a thick, "heavy" one. We decided to begin with the I.G. a campaign of joint development on the product to try to commercialize it for this purpose as soon as possible.

I went to the laboratories at the Oppau works the same afternoon to watch Vistanex being produced. The process was extremely interesting. Isobutylene was kept in open glass beakers packed in dry ice *—much as a grapefruit is served in a nest of cracked ice. Dry ice was also put into the beaker, where it dissolved in the isobutylene. Then the catalyzing gas was introduced into the beaker.

The reaction was more like a silent explosion than a normal chemical reaction. Upon the introduction of the catalyst, there was a slight puff, and the liquid in the beaker changed into a sponge of Vistanex of volume much greater than the liquid. It filled the beaker and bulged spectacularly out of the top. The sponge could be taken out at once and

* Carbon dioxide snow.

handled like a soft snowball. There was nothing left behind
in the beaker. This astonishing operation was all there was to
the manufacture of Vistanex, as it was then conducted.

The raw materials for Vistanex were another story. Germany had only a tiny oil refining industry and the amount of
isobutylene available was very small even though some practical means were to be developed for concentrating and purify-
ing it. Thus I.G. was compelled to produce isobutylene by
a costly chemical synthesis.

On my return to New York in May, 1932, I took with me
small samples of Vistanex and the data I.G. had given me on
its manufacture. The first step was to determine the properties and value of the heavier lubricating oils made by adding
Vistanex to lighter oils. There was noted at once an outstanding advantage of these oils—they were much less affected by
temperature changes than ordinary oils. This seemed to make
them especially suitable for automobile engines.

In cold weather the lubricating oil in an automobile engine
becomes so thick and viscous that it is almost impossible for
the starting battery to crank the motor. If an attempt is made
to avoid this difficulty by using a light oil in the engine,
lubrication fails when the engine gets hot, engine wear becomes excessive and the thin oil works past the piston and is
consumed at a high rate. The ideal automobile engine lubri-
cant, therefore, would be an oil which maintained the same
consistency at all temperatures.

By adding Vistanex to thin oil, this ideal was approached
better than ever before. Almost all the early tests were made in
Standard's laboratories, but in April, 1933, the Navy became
interested and undertook some tests. From this time on Standard was continuously in touch with the Navy, and later with
the Army, on these oils compounded with Vistanex. They
were used to some extent for general lubricating purposes, but
later became most widely used for hydraulic systems on air-

planes and warships and for gun recoil systems where wide temperature changes had to be provided for.

Standard began the sale of the Vistanex-treated oils in the winter of 1933-1934, using the trade name Paratone for liquid compounds of this type, and Vistanex for solid products.

For the initial production it was necessary to obtain isobutylene by chemical operations. At the same time, however, we began looking for methods of recovering the isobutylene present in refinery gases by more direct means without going through intermediate chemical processes.

At this stage, the thread of the synthetic rubber development crossed that of another important American technical development which has had a tremendous influence on world history. This latter development was the class of super-fuels known as "100-octane gasoline." In 1921, Midgley at the General Motors Research Laboratories had discovered that tetraethyl lead in minute proportions greatly improved the quality of gasoline; and, in 1923, Prof. C. A. Kraus, working for Standard's research laboratory, had discovered a cheap practical process to make the tetraethyl lead. Jointly with General Motors, Standard organized in 1924 the Ethyl Gasoline Corporation to undertake the commercial production and general sale of tetraethyl lead as an improver for motor gasoline. The miraculous effect of tetraethyl lead in preventing gasoline from knocking or "pinging" in an engine had by this time become the foundation for continuous improvement in gasoline engines. Each new engine design raised the compression pressure slightly, produced more power and gave more miles per gallon. But with each increment of compression pressure the tendency of the gasoline to knock became more aggravated, and the situation could be met only by improving the quality of the gasoline or by adding more tetraethyl lead —or both.

There was no established method for measuring the knocking tendency of gasoline. It was simply tried in the engine to determine whether it was good enough or not good enough. Dr. Graham Edgar of Ethyl Corporation's research laboratory met this need by working out in 1926 what was called an "octane scale." He tested the knocking tendency of every pure compound he could find which was of the general character of gasoline. The best compound was one called *iso-octane*. It would not knock under any condition in any engines then in use. At the other end of the scale was found a compound called *normal heptane*, which was so bad that it would knock violently in any engine. By mixing iso-octane and normal heptane in different proportions, it was possible to obtain fuels of any intermediate quality. The percentage of iso-octane in the mixture was called the "octane number" of that fuel. On this scale the quality of commercial gasolines could be rated by comparing them with various octane-heptane mixtures in a test engine. Commercial gasolines at this time had an octane rating ranging from 40 to 75. By the addition of tetraethyl lead, the best ones could be brought up to a maximum octane number of about 87.*

The octane scale created a demand for important quantities of iso-octane and normal heptane to be used for testing purposes for the rating of commercial gasolines. To fill this demand, the Ethyl Corporation asked Standard's research organization for assistance in the preparation of iso-octane. Iso-octane could be made by hydrogenating a twin isobutylene molecule (di-isobutylene) and the question was whether we could supply this product.

In 1929 we made the twin molecule for the Ethyl Corporation from mixtures of gases generated in our synthetic alcohol operations. It was converted to iso-octane by the classical hydrogenation methods.

By 1934 our research organization had a double problem on its hands. We needed increasing quantities of pure

* At the time of World War II the octane rating of American motor gasoline was from 70 to 85 and of aviation gasoline from 87 to 100.

isobutylene for production of the Vistanex, and there was also an increasing interest in producing super-fuels for automobile and airplane racing. Whenever anyone spoke of super-fuel, the obvious super-fuel was iso-octane itself, the standard of perfection by which gasoline was now being measured. In cooperation with the Ethyl Corporation, we had been producing it in small quantities for some years, for use as a fuel in laboratory test engines and the Shell Oil Company had also produced some and sold it to the Army Air Corps for test purposes. But the goal now was commercial production on a large scale as a super-fuel for automobile and airplane engines.

We solved both of these new commercial problems in 1935. The synthetic alcohol manufacturing which we had begun in 1919 was by this time a substantial industry. One of the steps in this operation was a preliminary purification of the refinery gases. By proper control of this operation, it was found possible to convert the isobutylene present in the gases into twins and triplets; that is, di-isobutylene and tri-isobutylene. We hydrogenated the twins to make iso-octane, using the I.G. high pressure hydrogenation technique slightly modified, and decomposed the triplets back to pure isobutylene by passing them over a catalyst. These processes worked smoothly and successfully from the beginning and provided at one stroke our raw materials for both Vistanex and iso-octane.

The iso-octane could be used alone as a fuel, but to obtain greater quantities and improve its volatility it was mixed with the best quality natural aviation gasoline fractions. The gasoline reduced the octane number of the mixture below 100, but it was brought back to 100 by the addition of tetraethyl lead.

The first 100-octane gasoline to be sold for commercial use was made up in this way at Standard's Baton Rouge refinery in June, 1935, and a small amount was delivered to Tulsa, Oklahoma, for use in the Southwest Air Races on June 29, 1935. Lt. Gen. James H. Doolittle, then a Major in the Air Corps Reserve, was, at this critical period in aviation history, manager of the aviation department of Shell Oil Company. Largely through Doolittle's foresight and aggressiveness, the Army had requested bids for a few cars of such a product as early as April of 1935 and the first delivery on this order was made by Shell to the Army in early July. From the time of its commercial debut in 1935, at the Southwest Air Races and in the Army Air Corps, 100-octane aviation gasoline became the synonym for maximum performance of airplane engines, military and civil. It was soon used all over the world for record-breaking flights and races, and the U.S. Army Air Corps, which had taken the lead in the development of high compression aviation engines, and which had placed its first order for 100-octane fuel even in advance of any commercial use, began to move toward standardizing all American military aviation on 100-octane fuel. Their tests indicated that 100-octane gasoline would permit roughly 20 per cent more power output, or, in the alternative, 15 per cent less gasoline consumption, in engines built to take full advantage of it.

So, by the middle of 1935, our technical organization in a close competitive race with that of Shell Oil Company had produced commercial synthetic iso-octane, which was used to make a super-fuel for aviation; and had at the same time gotten technically pure isobutylene, the raw material needed to make the new German discovery Vistanex.

In this year Vistanex assumed its final form as a rubber-like product made entirely from petroleum. The operation of causing isobutylene molecules to join into long chains at temperatures of 100° F. below zero had been improved and developed, and Vistanex of this quality was almost indistinguishable in appearance from natural crude rubber. But use of the product was still decidedly limited, because it could not be vulcanized. In addition, the Vistanex was still costly and difficult to make.

It was not until 1942, ten years after Standard had started the development, that we had what we regarded as a satisfactory large-scale operation running continuously. At the time of Standard's last contact with the I.G. on this question in 1939, they did not yet have any commercial operations which we thought equally satisfactory, and, so far as we knew, were still using the relatively expensive synthetic processes as a source of isobutylene.* Their commercial product was of the same quality as our own.

Since 1932 we had been doing laboratory research work on the synthesis of Vistanex and on chemical modifications of the product. We had exchanged information freely with the I.G. who were hard at work improving the Vistanex, but neither company had had any practical success in vulcanizing this polymer. The final solution of the vulcanizing problem was the result of a flank movement which came out at a wholly unexpected point. By 1937 Standard's technical organization, now separately incorporated under the name of Standard Oil Development Company, had become one of the largest industrial research organizations in the world with principal laboratories in Bayway, N. J., Baton Rouge, Louisiana and in London, England, and large affiliated laboratories in Texas and Canada. One Bayway laboratory, under the direction of Dr. Per K. Frolich,† who had come to us in 1929 from an associate professorship at the Massachusetts Institute of Technology, was devoted to chemical research in fields related to oil, as distinguished from the direct problems of oil refining. His staff had undertaken a broad investigation of low-temperature reactions. In the course of this work it was discovered that a small proportion of butadiene could

---

* Investigations made after the end of the war showed that they had continued to make their isobutylene in this way throughout the war.

† Dr. Frolich became President of the American Chemical Society in 1942.

be introduced into the isobutylene chain when it was formed. These butadiene molecules each had four free hands, only two of which were used to form the chain, leaving two free hands or "bonds" which could be used as cross-connectors. Mr. R. M. Thomas and Dr. W. J. Sparks, of the chemical staff, who had made this change in the Vistanex molecule, now succeeded in cross-tying the new composite chains by hitching sulphur across between the occasional butadiene links in one chain and those in another chain. This basic piece of work by Thomas and Sparks will always stand as one of the milestones of progress in synthetic rubber.

It was realized at once that the new product, which Standard christened "Butyl," might have great potentialities. The total isobutylene available in by-product refinery gases seemed sufficient to supply a very large demand. Isobutylene did not have to be made; it was already there and needed only to be separated. It ought to be available in great quantities at a few cents per pound. The butadiene needed was the same product required for Buna rubber, and was more expensive, but the amounts required for Butyl rubber were very small in proportion to the isobutylene used. Where Standard had already spent seven years trying, without much success, to make a start on the production of cheap butadiene for Buna synthetic rubber, it found the main raw material problem solved in advance in the case of Butyl.

There were, however, two other fundamental questions. How good a synthetic rubber could be made in this way, and how could the operation be carried out economically on a large industrial scale? These basic questions were posed in 1937. Through the succeeding years we hoped, experimented, predicted and estimated; but it was 1943 before we could demonstrate the first authoritative answers. Unfortunately these first answers, especially as to production cost, were not as favorable as earlier estimates.

In some respects, Butyl acts more like natural rubber than

does Buna, but it has both advantages and disadvantages when compared with either. It has a higher hysteresis or internal friction than either of the others, and in ordinary compounds it is not so strong. Its advantages are most apparent in its use as a tube.

These characteristics were recognized from the beginning, and because of them Butyl started under some handicaps. But, with the faith and optimism which must inspire a development program, Standard's technical organization was always sure that ways would ultimately be found to overcome the handicaps, and also to attain the low manufacturing costs which are clearly within the bounds of possibility. Sufficient progress was made in the first few years after Butyl was discovered to give a solid foundation for this belief.

During this early period of development it seemed probable that I.G. would be able to help us with Butyl because of their work on Vistanex, Buna, and synthetic rubber in general. Under our contracts of 1929 and 1930 they would become entitled, through the Joint Study Company, to a net participation of 37½ per cent in Butyl rubber when we had progressed far enough to initiate commercial testing and exploitation—just as we had become entitled to the same participation in their Buna development to the extent that it was based on oil or natural gas. However, while Butyl was an entirely new technical development and not merely an improvement on Vistanex, it was so near chemically to the Vistanex that we had reason to think the I.G. might learn how to make Butyl in their own research work. If they did that before we told them of our discovery, our rights as originators of the product would be prejudiced.* There was some fear in our organization that if we disclosed Butyl to the I.G. too soon, they might outdistance us in improv-

* Art. V of the Jasco agreement provided "The rule shall be that the party which first acquaints the other with the technical details of a new chemical process . . . shall be considered the originator. . . ."

ing it and then ask that our claim be compromised. The question never came up formally because the war intervened before Butyl had progressed far enough to be offered to the Joint Study Company but it must be said that they never gave indication of any such intention.

Butyl rubber, like its older sister Buna, had a troubled childhood. There were times when it gave promise of supplanting the Buna, and other times when it looked as though it never would be practical. Ultimately it became a very useful factor in the wartime synthetic rubber industry, second in importance only to Buna.

CHAPTER VI

THE LAST YEAR OF PEACE

On a visit to Germany in the early spring of 1938, I reviewed with Dr. ter Meer the status of the Buna rubber development. In the United States the interest in synthetic rubber was slowly increasing. Neoprene and Thiokol were by this time standard commercial products, although their total tonnage was less than one per cent of American rubber consumption.

It was clear to us now that there were two kinds of demand for synthetic rubber, and that these two demands involved quite different factors. The first was for basic or general-purpose rubber to compete directly with natural rubber; the second for new rubber-like products having certain properties quite different from natural rubber. Manufacturers would pay as much as $1 per pound for small amounts of these specialty rubbers, to be used in such products as gasoline hoses and valves and diaphragms in oil pumps—uses for which natural rubber is not satisfactory. In these cases the price of the synthetic rubber was a minor element in the cost of the finished product.

But this was not the type of industry that Standard Oil Company (N.J.) and the German I.G. Company had had in mind in carrying forward the work on Buna. We had been aiming at the natural rubber market—over 1,000,000 tons a year—not the specialty market of a few thousand tons. But others in America had been thinking mainly of this special market and during the preceding two years had made many inquiries of us. One company, which had a small but growing business in pipe couplings mainly used in the oil and gas industries, had been working assiduously with samples of Buna and was asking for exclusive rights to use it in their field. One of the leading manufacturers of chemical specialties for the rubber trade had applied for a contract as exclusive sales agent for Buna in the United States. Several American companies had approached us, indicating their interest in Buna as a specialty, and some of these same concerns also were making inquiries of the I.G. representatives in New York and the I.G. headquarters in Germany.

It was ter Meer's opinion that these American companies had no immediate interest in trying to advance the development of Buna rubber for general use as a replacement for natural rubber, but rather were interested only in obtaining an immediate profit or a competitive advantage in special lines. He pointed out that the German objective from the very beginning had been to develop a practical substitute for natural rubber in order to be independent of imports. This objective was deeply rooted in economic and military thinking in Germany. No such objective had influenced American thinking, save perhaps during the short period of resentment over the high prices resulting from the Stevenson crude rubber control plan.

After his discussion of this American situation Dr. ter Meer explained that the Buna development was moving along rapidly in Germany. All ideas of replacing Buna with neoprene had been put aside. Not only was the special quality of Buna known as Buna-N finding a small market, but the German rubber companies were by now experiencing less difficulty in handling Buna-S, the general-purpose rubber. The picture had changed to such an extent that I was encouraged to believe again that, with more time and effort, it might be economically feasible to introduce Buna as an all-purpose rubber in the United States.

Next we considered the situation arising from the fact that

the German government itself had been financing the Buna development in Germany. According to Dr. ter Meer, this meant that before I.G. could make any plans for a Buna manufacturing industry in the United States, they would have to consult their government. He feared that his government would reply that so far as the existing small demand of a ton or two a day of the special Buna-N product was concerned, it was more sensible to fill it by export from Germany than to attempt to manufacture on such a small scale in the United States. They might also urge that, because the development of Buna-S as an all-purpose rubber still had to be subsidized a premature attempt to promote it commercially and without any government subsidy in the United States would result in giving it a bad name which would handicap its acceptance later.

Acknowledging these factors, I told Dr. ter Meer I thought they were out-weighed by others. We felt, I told him, that even on a very small scale the Buna-N manufacturing industry could be successfully established in the United States as a competitor of Thiokol and neoprene. Also, while granting that it would take a great deal of patience, I thought the leading American rubber companies could be interested in some sound and practical cooperative arrangement for commercial development of a general-purpose synthetic rubber of the Buna-S type, even though it might cost initially more than natural rubber.

All the Buna rubber made up to this time had come from coal and not from oil, and we therefore had no claim on the German acetylene process; I.G. was not obliged to submit it to the Joint Study Company. I reminded ter Meer, however, that our two companies had proceeded since 1930 on the assumption that, in the United States at least, Buna would be made from oil or natural gas, if it were produced on any large scale, and that accordingly both parties had always considered it to be in substance, if not in form, within the Joint

Study Agreement. I reminded him also that we had spent more than three-quarters of a million dollars as our share in the Baton Rouge arc acetylene process and related developments; that we were warranted in holding that these considerations gave us a right to insist that the Joint Study Company should now attempt to organize an American group to take over the whole Buna development here.

Dr. ter Meer agreed that our position was reasonable and justified, and promised that he would present this point of view to his associates and, if they agreed, to his government. Ter Meer acknowledged at this time that, for some reason which he did not explain, the German government had not previously been informed that the Joint American Study Company was entitled to Buna rights outside of Germany. He intimated that in view of the large expenditures the government had made in Germany in perfecting Buna, it might be somewhat embarrassing now to break the news that foreign rights had long ago been contracted for. He was sure, however, that if the matter were handled tactfully no serious difficulties would arise on this account.

When our discussion of the Buna situation was finished, I reviewed with Dr. ter Meer our new development, Butyl. We had filed our patent application in the U.S. Patent Office the preceding year, and would be compelled to file it in England, France, Germany and other foreign countries within a few months to protect our patent rights there. Ter Meer's reaction was satisfactory. He raised no question of the relation of our Butyl to their Vistanex. He complimented us on an outstanding piece of chemical development, but very quickly put his finger on the weak spots. He asked especially about the hysteresis characteristics of the Butyl rubber—that is whether it had high or low internal friction. I told him it was quite high. He shook his head, and said that was the fundamental point to attack, as in their long experimentation with the Buna types they had found high hysteresis to be the most stubborn characteristic of a synthetic rubber. The years of subsequent work with Butyl proved him to be right.

Before we parted, ter Meer and I had agreed upon a working program. He was to attempt to convince his own associates and, if they agreed, then inform the German government that steps should be taken to initiate a commercial Buna development in the United States, without waiting further to perfect the operation or the product in Germany. We both were to review our butadiene-from-oil experimentation, and I.G. was to start intensive work on what looked to be one of the best processes for the chemical treatment of butylene derived from oil to convert it into butadiene. I.G. was to study the preliminary reports I was leaving on Butyl in the light of their own work on Vistanex and give us any suggestions they might have. We were to proceed actively with our own Butyl development program.

Almost immediately after my return to New York, in the spring of 1938, Dr. Sebrell of the Goodyear Tire and Rubber Company called to tell me that his company was discussing arrangements with the Dow Chemical Company to proceed jointly in the manufacture of synthetic rubber and that they would like to talk to us about Buna. I went at once to call on Mr. Paul W. Litchfield, President of Goodyear, whose long experience and position made him one of the outstanding personalities of the American rubber industry.

Mr. Litchfield was definite and firm. He wanted the Joint Study Company to name terms for an exclusive license to Goodyear under all the Buna patents. He was especially interested in proceeding at once with some production of Buna N, which he considered superior to Buna S, even for tires. He backed up his position with a very convincing statement of the strength, resources, and ability of his organization and the progress already made in their own laboratories in producing Buna type rubbers. Dr. R. P. Dinsmore, technical vice president of Goodyear, had been one of the earliest

American workers in the synthetic rubber field and a pioneer in the laboratory use of the important emulsion polymerization process which the I.G. had developed commercially. The pending Dow affiliation, Mr. Litchfield urged, made the Goodyear position even more dominant.

Much as I was impressed by the force and sincerity of Mr. Litchfield, I felt that it would be a fatal mistake to grant an exclusive license to one of the great rubber companies. The effect would certainly be to alienate all the others. Buna could never become a great industry against the determined opposition of the bulk of the rubber trade and it seemed doubtful whether Goodyear would do anything at all about Buna S production. My own associates and the I.G. agreed when I reported this talk to them.

In the summer of that same year (1938), I returned to Europe, primarily on business matters pending in France. Among these was the completion of plans to manufacture chemical products from refinery gases. Discussions had been going on for months between Standard's refining subsidiary in France, Standard Francaise des Petroles, and the French chemical firm, Usines de Melle, looking toward a joint venture in this field. Immediate action was necessary because the French government was calling for the manufacture of a product known as iso-propyl ether, for use in aviation gasoline as a substitute for iso-octane. Standard's technical organization in the United States had developed a process for making it. It could not compete economically with other synthetic blending agents for 100 octane gasoline then available in the United States, but its manufacture in France fitted into the general plan for producing alcohols* there and was in accord with the growing desire for self-sufficiency of the great European nations, a desire aggravated by the fear that if war

---

* Iso-propyl ether is best made as a part of a synthetic alcohol development.

came in Europe, America would, under its then existing "Neutrality Act," * cut off war supplies to all the belligerents.

During this visit I spent a weekend at Deauville with some American friends who had lived in France for many years. By this time European politics had become the standard subject for weekend conversation. The main question was, of course, what Germany's real intentions and aspirations were.

This led to talk of the military strength of Germany. The general sentiment was that, however strong her armies might be and however difficult it might be to conquer Germany by direct military action, she would be doomed to certain defeat through a blockade which would cut off necessary imports.

I had noted this same point of view in England among my friends there. It seemed to me that these opinions reflected the past rather than the present and I could not help wondering whether the responsible government officials of England, France and the United States were really up to date on the advances made in industrial science since the first World War.

I was going directly from Deauville to Berlin and made up my mind that the first thing I should do there would be to call on the American Ambassador, Hugh Wilson, and discuss this question with him. Upon my arrival in Berlin a few days later, I dropped a note to Ambassador Wilson and an appointment was arranged almost at once.

I informed the Ambassador that the purpose of my visit was to tell him what I knew about Germany's scientific progress in the production of raw materials which she normally had to import. In the first World War Germany had been strangled by a blockade which cut her off from imports without which no nation could either live or wage war. There were many items in the list, but perhaps the four most important were oil, rubber, fats and textile fibers. I reviewed scientific progress in Germany along these lines since 1918. As to

* Neutrality Act of 1935, amended May 1, 1937.

synthetic fibers, my information was only secondhand and general. On the other three, I had considerable first-hand knowledge of what had been done and a fair idea of what Germany could accomplish in case of need.

I described first the processes for producing oil from coal. At the rate at which this development was being pushed forward in Germany, there was no doubt that she would have, in the event of war, a very large internal supply of the highest quality of oil products, with the possible exception of lubricating oils. Germany not only could make good base stock for aviation gasoline* by coal hydrogenation, but she could also make the American product tetraethyl lead further to improve its quality. A tetraethyl lead plant had, I knew, been erected in Germany in 1936 under licenses approved by the American State Department after consultation with the War and Navy Departments.

In the case of lubricating oils, there were some very recent synthetic developments other than hydrogenation which had not been publicized as yet, but which were producing small quantities of the best quality aviation lubricating oils, and I knew something of the plans which were being made to increase this production.

As to synthetic fats, the problem had not been entirely solved, but substantial progress had been made in the production of synthetic paraffin from coal and in the conversion of this paraffin into synthetic fatty acids. The fatty acids were not the equal of the fatty acids of animal and vegetable origin used by the soap industry and by some special branches of the chemical industry, but they were good enough to replace natural fatty acids in emergency. The result would be that practically the entire supply of animal and vegetable fats in Germany could be used for food, while the very large indus-

---

* Her principal handicap was lack of any large supply of the by-product refining gases from which iso-octane and other aviation blending stocks were made. Because of this handicap Germany could not standardize on blended 100-octane aviation gasoline of the American type.

trial requirements, of which the greatest was soap manufacture, could be supplied by the synthetic fatty acids.

Last of all there was the matter of rubber. I reported to the Ambassador that the German government had been pushing the I.G. Buna development for some years, that they had a production of several thousand tons a year and had plans for substantial increases. While Buna was not as good as natural rubber, it showed such imminent promise of being a suitable rubber for tires and general purposes that the type of rubber famine from which Germany had suffered in the first World War would, in my opinion, never be repeated.

The Ambassador stated that the Embassy had general knowledge of all these matters, but was particularly glad to obtain this confirmation, and to learn that further detailed information could be obtained from us at any time by the State Department in America or by the U.S. Embassy in London from our general European organization which centered in London and of which the key personnel was American. I also called the Ambassador's attention to the fact that the Dutch-British Royal Dutch Shell group of oil companies had full information on technical oil developments in Germany through their license contracts with Standard Oil Company (N.J.) and with the I.G., and that the General Motors Corporation, which owned the largest motor car factory in Germany, the Opel Plant, was also half owner with Standard of the Ethyl Corporation, and through these channels could also supply some direct information to the American government concerning Germany's internal strength. I expressed to him my fear that neither the Americans, the English, nor even the French correctly estimated the potential ability of Germany to withstand the type of blockade which had contributed so much to her downfall in the last war.

After we had covered the subject between ourselves, the Ambassador called in the Second Secretary of the Embassy whose special province was economic and industrial questions.

The Ambassador asked me if I could assist the Secretary in preparing a report on our conversation for forwarding to the State Department. The Secretary and I agreed that the best form would be a chart of the synthetic processes which Germany had developed and the foreign companies interested in these developments and through whom information might be obtained. A rough chart was supplied by me the same day, and the Secretary advised me that he intended to send it with an explanatory letter to the Department. In 1942 when the matter became active in another connection, it appeared that the chart and explanatory letter had been duly forwarded to Washington on November 4, 1938. They are reproduced in the Appendix.*

While in Berlin on this trip I learned from the I.G. directors there that ter Meer had reported to his associates our discussions of the early spring, that they all agreed with our conclusions, and that there had already been some favorable reactions from the government officials to whom they had talked during that summer of 1938. They felt they had made good progress in explaining the situation to their government and would soon be able to work out with us a plan to introduce Buna into the United States.

But just when the road to the start of a commercial Buna industry in the United States seemed to be clearing up, a new hazard appeared. Dr. Herman Schmitz, financial leader of the I.G., told me that one of their directors had conceived the idea that the most money with the least risk could be made out of the Buna development by selling it to the Dutch-British interests in London who dominated the rubber trade through the International Rubber Regulation Agreement. It was argued that these interests would be willing to buy the synthetic rubber development in order to hold up the price of

---

* Appendix p. 261. In the report of the Senate Committee for the Investigation of the War Program it is erroneously stated that this chart was made at the Hague in 1939.

their natural rubber. I opposed this suggestion at once as a short-sighted plan, probably impractical, and in any event out of line with the policies of my company, and, so far as my experience went, also out of line with the policies of I.G. The production executives of the I.G. to whom I talked had the same view, as did Standard's Executive Committee, to whom I reported this suggestion on October 28, 1938.* I never heard anything more of it.

I.G. had undertaken, pursuant to my agreement with ter Meer earlier in the year, to test a new chlorination process for converting butylene derived from oil into butadiene. They had in operation a pilot plant in which they were processing samples of butylene obtained as a by-product from Standard's American refineries.

Results were fairly satisfactory, and the process represented a forward step in that it made possible initial production of butadiene in the United States with less equipment than previous processes. The chlorination process appeared definitely superior under American conditions to the arc acetylene process on which we had spent so much money at Baton Rouge. A variant of this chlorination process was actually used to make small tonnages of butadiene from oil gases in the United States by the Shell Oil Company in 1941.

The Munich crisis of 1938 overtook me in London on my way home. When it was over there was, for a time, an optimistic feeling that any further immediate troubles in Europe would be only minor ones. I had been back only a short time when word came from Dr. ter Meer that his government had now stated that it had no objection to the introduction of the Buna development into the United States. Dr. ter Meer was himself coming to initiate the discussions, and asked me to arrange meetings with some of the American rubber companies. We accordingly arranged appointments for him with the five rubber companies who had shown the most interest

* Appendix, p. 264.

in Buna—Firestone, General Tire and Rubber, Goodrich, Goodyear and United States Rubber.

Dr. ter Meer arrived in November, 1938. The American companies were at this time interested primarily in Buna as a specialty business. Only the Buna-N type was of immediate commercial value to them. Dr. ter Meer was convinced, on the basis of German experience, that the future of Buna as an industry lay not with Buna-N, but with Buna-S. It was easier to make than Buna-N, for the only raw material needed besides butadiene was styrene, a chemical obtainable at relatively low cost. Also, Buna-S had been tested extensively in tires in Germany and, although it was not 100 per cent successful as a substitute for natural rubber, there was no question but that excellent tires could be made with as much as 70 per cent of Buna and 30 per cent of natural rubber, with every prospect that the natural rubber content could be much further reduced and even eliminated for light tires. Improvements had been made in handling Buna-S, and it was now reported by German rubber companies that, by a new pretreatment process which Dr. ter Meer described to us, it could be fabricated in regular tire factory machinery much more easily than Buna-N, and almost as well as natural rubber.

Dr. ter Meer brought with him data covering a long series of tests which were just being completed in Germany showing the relative wear of Buna-S tires as against natural rubber tires. This test program had been initiated and controlled by the German government and was far more complete than anything previously available. Dr. ter Meer reviewed these tests, which showed Buna-S tires to have in many cases longer average tread wear than natural rubber—in some cases as much as 30 per cent more. His plan was, therefore, to interest the American rubber companies in the use of Buna-S as a tread material on their highest grade passenger car tires, perhaps to be sold at a premium price.

A first quality tire used on light passenger cars contained

about 12 pounds of rubber, only 4 pounds being in the tread, but it was then the American custom to throw away passenger car tires or sell them as junk when the tread had worn smooth. Therefore, the life of the tire in the hands of the consumer was simply the life of the tread. If this tread could be made to wear 25 per cent longer, the whole tire would have a 25 per cent higher value to the motorist. The retail price of such a tire was then about $12. With 25 per cent more mileage, it would be worth $3 more. Assuming that natural rubber would cost 10 cents less per pound than Buna-S, the extra cost of the tread might be 40 cents but it would be worth $3 extra to the motorist. In addition, such tires would become recognized as the standard of highest quality, an asset to any tire manufacturer.

This line of reasoning was not new, but Dr. ter Meer now believed he had the data to prove that it was correct. His plan was to take advantage of the immediate financial interest which the American companies were displaying in the Buna-N type of rubber to interest them in the manufacture of Buna-S on a large scale for use as a tread stock. If this could be done, we should finally have arrived at our original goal of starting a real synthetic rubber industry in the United States—not merely as a small volume specialty business which would have costs too high to permit it to compete with natural rubber, but as a relatively large-volume product.

Dr. ter Meer opened his discussions with the five American rubber companies during December, 1938. The first question, of course, was the quality of Buna-S. Was it good enough to be practical in tires which had to be sold in the competitive market? Would it give superior mileage?

The rubber companies had all had long experience in testing tires, but this was a field in which it was particularly difficut to reconcile test results. It was not recognized as clearly then as it was later that this difficulty was largely due to the difference between results obtained in hard service and those obtained in mild service.

In early 1939, when this matter was under discussion between the I.G. and the American rubber companies, inconsistencies in test results had been observed, but their explanation was not agreed upon. The American companies wanted to run tests of their own, and ter Meer agreed to send each of them necessary quantities of the latest type of Buna-S rubber and also an expert, experienced in the compounding, fabrication and vulcanizing of Buna-S tires. When ter Meer left in January, 1939, this program had been set, and was subsequently carried through.

The German expert, Dr. Koch, arrived early in 1939, and proceeded in turn to the factories and laboratories of the rubber companies where test tires were being made up. The regular New York representatives of I.G. followed the work closely and from time to time advised us verbally of the progress being made. Some of the companies had completed their tests, and all were well along on them before the outbreak of the war in Europe in September, 1939. The results were on the whole favorable and were accepted as general confirmation of the German tests reported by Dr. ter Meer. To stimulate interest in synthetic rubber in the United States, the I.G. expert, Dr. Koch, presented a scientific paper on the Buna rubber to the meeting of the Rubber Section of the American Chemical Society in Baltimore in April, 1939.

During these months in which the American rubber industry was checking the German tests of the latest Buna rubber, the international political situation was deteriorating rapidly. The public, the press, the Congress, and the Administration—all seemed determined that our nation must not again be drawn into the European maelstrom. But war was in the air. We in Standard knew that the Ass't. Secretary of War, Lewis Johnson, was making a hard fight to establish an industrial preparedness program, and that with his backing the Army and Navy Munitions Board was trying to complete a survey of American production potentialities in case of war.

With the thought that we might be helpful, early in January, 1939, I called on Mr. Johnson and on Colonel Charles Hines, then Secretary of the Army and Navy Munitions Board, to inquire as to their interest in rubber, and also talked to Colonel H. K. Rutherford, the Secretary's aide responsible for these studies. I was told that rubber was on their list of "strategic materials" and that they would be glad to have any information we could supply on producing it synthetically. I promised to have Dr. Frolich, Director of Standard's chemical research laboratories at Bayway, call on the Board. Dr. Frolich made his first visit a few days later, on January 12, 1939, and reviewed for the Munitions Board the three types of rubber on which Standard had special knowledge: Buna-N, Buna-S and our Butyl, which we were identifying at that time by the code name of "Buna-X."

From the time of these first visits Standard's organization was continuously in touch with the Army and Navy Munitions Board until its functions in connection with rubber were transferred to the Advisory Committee to the Council of National Defense in January, 1940. The early interest of the Board was both in the quality of synthetic products for special military purposes, and in the possibility of developing American production. The interest of the various bureaus of the Army and Navy was more specific and limited. They wished to know just how good each type of synthetic rubber would prove to be for each kind of service in which rubber was used by the armed forces and did not concern themselves with the overall supply position. There was no indication that either the economic or military policy of the nation as yet included any plan actually to prepare for the possibility that we might be cut off from our supply of natural rubber.

I went back to Europe in February, 1939, primarily to find some way through a difficult situation which had arisen in

France in connection with the French Army's attempts to have high quality aviation gasoline produced there. The French subsidiaries of the Royal Dutch-Shell group and of Standard Oil Company (N.J.) had contracted jointly to build for the French Army a large high-pressure hydrogenation plant following the I.G. process and similar to the German, English and American plants. These plants could produce aviation base stock of the highest quality from any available petroleum product—from motor gasoline, kerosene, gas oil, or even fuel oil or coal tar. But the project was being held up. The source of the delays, hitherto inexplicable, was discovered by early 1939 to lie in a movement backed wholly by French nationals, to obtain financial help from their government for the local oil industry. It was hoped to link the French Army's plan to produce aviation gasoline with a government subsidy for modernizing the French oil industry's refining equipment. Some of the refineries were interested in installing a new process of French origin which had good commercial possibilities and would also make aviation gasoline.

The matter of providing for an emergency aviation gasoline supply in France had therefore been taken out of the Army's Service des Poudres with whom we had been cooperating and was now in the hands of the Minister of Public Works.

It was my own conviction that the French commercial interests who had brought about this change of government policy, however sincere their beliefs as to the best technical and economic procedure to be used to produce aviation gasoline in France, had overlooked the fact that what was most needed was speed and certainty. If detailed plans developed by the Army during the preceding two years were discarded and an attempt made to start afresh on a commercial program, the result would certainly be delay.

I expressed this view, but soon afterwards the cabinet promulgated a "decree law" which offered to all French refineries a subsidy to be applied toward construction of any new equipment capable of producing aviation gasoline. The Royal Dutch-Shell subsidiary undertook to proceed with a hydrogenation plant at its own refinery under this law, but the plans for the original large hydrogenation project which had been worked out for the Army had to be completely redrawn and the delay was so great that nothing useful was accomplished in time. Standard's operating subsidiary in France decided to try to save time by using a newly developed operation called "hydroforming," which was akin to hydrogenation but did not require the costly hydrogen plant. Hydroforming converted low quality motor gasoline into high quality motor gasoline or into a smaller yield of aviation gasoline. The process was based upon inventions of the I.G. which Standard had acquired in our 1929 purchase and had further worked out in cooperation with others in the United States. We not only undertook to build this equipment in our own large and modern refinery in France but quickly made agreements with the French subsidiary of the Anglo-Iranian Oil Company (controlled by the British government), and the Compagnie Francaise (controlled by the French government) to license the process to them. Designs were to be standardized so that all three refineries could build at maximum speed.

The immediate endorsement and acceptance by the refineries controlled by the British and French governments of the substitute aviation gasoline program, which our technical organization had so quickly worked out in an effort to make the best of a bad matter, gave a flying start to the new program, but it proved to be too late to accomplish anything of value in the defense of France.

From Paris I went to Germany in the spring of 1939 to check up personally on the butadiene program, which some of our chemical engineers had been following actively with the I.G. people. I visited the pilot plant at the I. G. Oppau works near Mannheim, where butadiene was being produced by the chlorination process from refinery butylene supplied by Standard. The pilot operation was now working very well, and I was given technical reports and designs for this process.

On my return to the United States in the late spring of 1939, the first order of business was another technical development in which the I.G. was actively interested, and which also played a part in the rubber drama. This was catalytic cracking.

Chapter VII

WAR IN EUROPE

For the world at large the summer of 1939 marked the slow eclipse of "peace in our time." For Standard's technical organization it was a summer of hard work and vexing problems. Laboratory experimentation on Butyl was being pressed at an expenditure of about $10,000 per month. Hoping for agreement on a program for Buna manufacture the following winter, we were busy with plans to produce its raw material, butadiene. In addition, the Ordnance Department of the U.S. Army was depending upon our group to develop a process for large-scale production of synthetic toluene—a complicated operation which, like our French plant for producing aviation gasoline, was an offshoot of the German hydrogenation process but which, in the development stage, involved altering and combining manufacturing operations at refineries in Louisiana, Texas and New Jersey, and shuttling trains of tank cars from one to the other to take advantage of special equipment at each place.

At the same time we were trying to reconcile varying interests within a group called Catalytic Research Associates. This group included three foreign companies—I. G. Farben-industrie, the British Anglo-Iranian Oil Company and the Dutch-British Royal Dutch-Shell Company; three American oil companies—the Texas Company, Standard Oil Company (Indiana) and our own company; and two American process development organizations operating in the oil industry—The M. W. Kellogg Company and the Universal Oil Products Company. All were interested in the catalytic treatment of oils. Each had technical contributions to make. The group was trying to arrive at some workable arrangement under which they could exchange their knowledge and supplement one another's research efforts in catalytic refining, and each could secure the right to use or to license the processes resulting from the combined efforts.

Although now common in industry, there is probably no more difficult form of arrangement to negotiate than a co-operative research and development contract providing for cross-licensing of patents between industrial units. When eight companies of four nationalities attempt such a task, the difficulty becomes monumental. Robert P. Russell, then executive vice president of the Standard Oil Development Company, and Frederick R. Loofbourow, our European legal specialist, labored with me in this Tower of Babel for weeks before the negotiators' memorandum was initialed. It proved to have been time well spent, however, because out of the research which was contemplated by these negotiations there finally evolved the Fluid Catalytic Cracking Process, which Standard brought to successful completion and which later contributed in a most important way to the nation's desperate need for 100 octane gasoline and synthetic rubber.

The day after these memoranda were signed in August, 1939, I left for Europe by plane, proceeding directly to Paris to pick up the threads of the project for building Standard's newest type aviation gasoline plants in the French refineries of the French Government's Company, the British Government's Company and our own subsidiary company. Mr. W. C. Asbury, who had become Standard's chief refinery technologist in Europe, and Mr. W. R. Carlisle, our American counsel in London, met me there, and a program was laid out for the engineering and contract work in France. I then left for Vichy, intending to take a two weeks' holiday.

One week later the Nazis marched into Poland. Just off the Central Park in Vichy, regular news bulletins had roared from a loudspeaker sponsored by a local newspaper. The tension had increased daily and the crowds in front of the loudspeaker had grown with the tension. When the blow finally fell on August 31, one could almost feel its physical impact on the crowd. As the general mobilization order was announced, the loud buzz of innumerable conversations ended in stricken silence. The hush was broken by a few gasps and sobs and the crowd melted away.

Railroads were immediately taken over by the army and all timetables suspended. Long-distance telephone service was cut off. Mail was censored by the simple expedient of holding it indefinitely in the post office before delivering it. There was no possibility of moving or of consulting my associates in Paris—nothing to do for a few days but try to get oriented in this new world of war.

Like every American, I thought of the critical problems which the coming of war in Europe forced us to face at home. Surely the United States would now have to begin industrial and military preparedness on a great scale. This should mean forced-draft development of new processes and plants useful in a defense effort. Aviation gasoline and synthetic toluene were certain to be critical problems. What about rubber?

I considered the Buna development. After nearly ten years of effort it had just now arrived at the point of being ready for launching in the United States. But Buna was a German invention, patented in our own U.S. Patent Office by I.G. Farbenindustrie. Its commercialization in the United States under the existing arrangements would have to be a joint enterprise undertaken through the Joint Study Company, and on all Buna questions I.G. would have the deciding voice because it was their original process. As matters stood, we could do nothing alone. The United States government could of course act in complete disregard of the patents, no matter who owned them. This inherent right had been specifically confirmed by a special statute many years before. But there was no existing governmental machinery capable of establishing a synthetic rubber industry. Private initiative and private industry would have to plan and carry through any such development and about all it could hope for from the government was financial help.

Also, there was the matter of documents of assignment or grant for a great number of patents in which Standard had an interest but which had originated with the I.G. Several thousands of them had been involved in the 1929 agreement and the supplementary 1930 agreement. They included all existing patents of the I.G. relating to oil throughout the world except Germany. They included also those dealing with oil-chemical industries.

In handling these patents, the usual procedure had been to rely on the general contracts and postpone execution or recording of formal documents covering the separate patents until some business reason made these steps necessary. The situation was further complicated by the fact that the right of the two American patent holding companies, Standard-I.G. Company and the Joint Study Company (Jasco), to many of the most important patents, including Buna patents, was in many cases an exclusive right under the patent for the defined purposes only, with I.G. having the exclusive right under the patent for all other purposes. The detailed procedure was established by the 1929 contract for the oil patents. If the patent were mainly useful for the processes which belonged to us, it was to be assigned to us, leaving I.G. with a reserved exclusive license for itself for all processes it had not sold to us, and conversely, if uses in our defined field were not the principal ones dealt with in the patent, I.G. would keep the title and we would have the exclusive license only in our defined field. It was often difficult to decide which was the greater and which the lesser use of the patent. In the case of the oil-chemical patents, the parties had disregarded all formalities while proceeding with the development work. For these various reasons, the two patent holding companies had, during the preceding ten years, taken separate assignments to less than half of the total patents to which they were entitled in whole or in part by the blanket provisions of our 1929 purchase agreement with I.G. We had, during recent troubled months, been trying to clear up the records on more of these patents, but a great number of separate formal documents were still needed.

At this time, of course, the United States was not at war with Germany. Diplomatic and trade relations continued and normal legal procedures had to be observed. However, a blockade by the British fleet, which would unquestionably be instituted, might make it difficult or even impossible to obtain delivery of legal documents from Germany, or to communicate freely as had been our custom on technical and patent problems involved in our contracts with the I.G.

It was clear that Standard would have to adjust itself at once to an entirely new set of conditions which might last a short time or a long time, and might or might not eventually involve our own country in the war. The thing to do seemed to be to try our best to arrange matters so that we could carry forward without delay or interruption, alone and entirely independent of I.G. if necessary, all of the important technical developments which came under our 1929 and 1930 contracts and which, by those contracts, had been envisioned as being handled through jointly owned American companies in the management of which the parties would actively cooperate.

From Vichy, I cabled Mr. William S. Farish, who had now succeeded Mr. Teagle as President of Standard, as follows: "Seems best await developments risking considerable delay in return because should work out at Hague best possible modus vivendi development problems. Also seems probable you may have other requirements direct representation there."

Through our French subsidiary and with the help of the French authorities, I was able to proceed to London as soon as the first mobilization load was off the railways. There I reviewed the situation with our counsel, Mr. Carlisle, who was familiar with every detail of the I.G. contracts. I had already cabled New York asking that they try to arrange an appointment with Von Knieriem of I.G. for me in Holland and that he bring assignments of all patents in which we held interests. In London, I asked the American Embassy whether it would be proper for me to go to Holland to meet the I.G. representatives and get all possible help in clearing up our record titles and to discuss with them how to handle our contract relations. Mr. Herschel V. Johnson, a career diplomat who was then counsellor of the Embassy,* was doubtful of the propriety of an American citizen going to Holland to talk to England's enemies and then returning immediately to England.

I could not escape the conviction, however, that the Germans themselves were the only people who could profit from a military standpoint by leaving the relations between Standard and the I.G. in the situation into which the war had thrown them. If the right of Standard to use and license others to use these valuable processes which had originated in Germany, but which Standard knew more about than anyone else outside of Germany, were left clouded by lack of any formal documents, the effect might be to handicap the production of several important munitions of war in the world outside of Germany. Who but the Germans could derive any military benefit from this situation? Mr. Johnson saw these difficulties and referred the matter to Ambassador Joseph P. Kennedy. The Ambassador discussed the problem with us and decided that it was proper for Standard to try to obtain from the Germans documents needed to give it the freest possible hand in the exploitation of the German processes, especially in the United States. He could see no reason for the British to object. I told the Ambassador that to reassure the

---

* Later an Ambassador in several capitals.

British I would be glad to have all my discussions with the Germans in Holland take place in the presence of a representative of the American legation at The Hague. The British Foreign Office, however, had no objection to my going to Holland to meet the Germans and returning at once to England, and saw no necessity for the presence of an American government official to chaperon these business discussions.

I went alone to The Hague on September 22. There I met Dr. Fritz Ringer, a young I.G. chemical executive who had been handling many of their contract matters with us for several years. His only companion was a junior lawyer from their patent department. Von Knieriem, their legal chief, had been unable to come.

They had brought with them long lists of patent assignments covering all the principal countries of the world. There had been no time to consider each patent in detail. They said that wherever it appeared that the patent seemed to come under our contracts, they had brought the assignment and that they had confidence in our willingness to rectify any errors which might appear on careful checking of the contracts and patents. They asked only that I acknowledge that they remained entitled, under these patents, to all licensing rights not sold by the original contracts and at the same time gave me their assurance that if they had overlooked any patent in which we held rights, they would correct the error.* This voluntary action on their part solved the worst problem involved in the patents by clearing all the record titles. It created some secondary legal problems but we were able to find

* Text of their assurance read "Similarly it may have happened, though we do not think it probable, that one case or other actually coming within the scope of our agreement has been left out from the assignments by mistake. In such a case we, of course, maintain the view that your contractual rights thereunder are not in any way modified. We are, of course, quite prepared to correct such a mistake if it should have happened by making out an appropriate assignment."

solutions to all these secondary problems after my return to the United States.

There was one minor difficulty which became important only because of its unfortunate effect in contributing to the confusion during the Congressional investigations of the synthetic rubber problem in 1942. The assignments of French patents lacked the necessary certificate of the French consul-general in Berlin, his office having of course been closed on the day of the outbreak of the war.

I discussed this problem with Mr. George Gordon, the American Minister at The Hague. Mr. Gordon pointed out that the United States consulate in Berlin had taken over the legal duties of the French consulate. The necessary certificate could therefore be executed by the American consul in Berlin and, if the State Department in Washington would consent, the diplomatic courier could pick up the assignments at the American Embassy in Berlin and deliver them to the American Embassy in Paris. From there they could be taken to the French patent office. This seemed a workable plan, and the Minister started to prepare a cable to the State Department covering the situation. He told me it would be necessary to include in the cable information concerning the identity of the companies and the nature of the documents. I recalled my discussion with Ambassador Wilson in Berlin just one year before, concerning the German technical developments to which these assignments related. The Ambassador had certainly intended to make a report on these matters to the State Department. If he had done so, it seemed likely that his report would identify sufficiently the parties concerned and show the importance of the patent assignments in question. Minister Gordon thought this a good solution and confined his cable to our request for assistance in the delivery of these assignments, mentioning the report probably make a year earlier from Berlin by Ambassador Wilson as a source of more complete information. A reply was received authorizing the transmission of the assignments from Berlin to Paris by diplomatic courier, a procedure which went through according to schedule within the succeeding few weeks. These circumstances, and a coincidence in dates, later led one of the Congressional Committees to state erroneously that the report from Berlin of 1938 had originated at the Hague in 1939.*

As soon as all the patent assignments had been checked for form and delivered to me, and while Dr. Ringer and I were awaiting word from Washington on the French assignments, we took up the problem of the Joint American Study Company which was entitled to the exclusive right to the synthetic chemical processes. The situation confronting us was a difficult one. We had organized an American corporation, owned equally by the I.G. and Standard and intended as a vehicle for commercializing these new processes for making chemical products from oil or gas. Each company had to put up the capital required in equal amounts, but the company originating a process had a five-eighths net interest in the proceeds (after repayment of the expenses of development) and the right to decide upon the program with respect to its development.

So far, the Joint Study Company had undertaken active work on several developments, all originating with I.G. I.G. had the deciding voice on each of them and nothing could be done without its consent. Although the United States was not at war with Germany, we both feared that unless something were done, the Joint Study Company's business would be likely to stand still until peace came to the world again, whenever that might be.

The Vistanex process had gotten involved in complications which had been taken care of temporarily by an agreement which permitted Standard to carry on the business commer-

* See note on p. 68.

cially, an agreed royalty being paid directly to I.G. On the synthetic fatty acid and all aspects of the Buna processes no definitive commercial arrangements of any kind had yet been made but Dr. Ringer knew of the plans on which we had just been working with ter Meer to start a Buna development in the United States.

The most obvious solution was for Standard to buy out for cash the I.G.'s entire interest in the Joint Study Company and related contracts, and then proceed entirely on its own responsibility and with its own money.

The first difficulty here was the uncertainty as to the values involved. I did not know how much I.G. had spent in developing their processes, but it certainly was many millions. Presumably they would not want to sell at a loss. On the other hand, I did not believe Standard's Board of Directors would wish to buy for a large amount in cash the German interest in these new processes of which only one, the Vistanex process, had yet demonstrated any earning power.

And, as I considered it, there was another strong argument against a cash purchase. Although the United States was committed to a policy of formal neutrality in the war which had just begun, American sympathies were definitely not with Germany. Whatever the commercial considerations might be, I felt sure that Standard would hesitate to make a large cash payment to a German concern at this time. There was not yet any control of foreign exchange in the United States and any such payment made to German nationals would become at once available for use by their government to aid it in prosecuting the war.

Another possible solution occurred to me. Standard might trade its three-eighths interest in the processes in a part of the world for I.G.'s five-eighths interest in other parts of the world.

It was obvious that the German stock interest in the Joint Study Company would present a real problem in France and England during the war, and that, whatever the outcome of the war, any German business interest would be unpopular in those countries for years afterward. Standard, however, wished to proceed with the new processes in both of these countries as well as in the United States, and was under no present or prospective handicap. On the other hand, the I.G. might wish (or find themselves urged by their government) to have the Joint Study Company proceed actively in Italy, Spain, Japan, or even Russia, on some of these processes. We had a contract right to be informed, and could object, but could not block such action.

It looked as though it would suit both parties best if we could part company through a trade of some kind, each party getting free of an embarrassment and clearing his own road. Since Standard had the minority interest and also wanted to keep the United States rights as its part of the trade, it looked as though we would have to give up our interest not only in the countries which were definitely in Germany's orbit, including Russia at that time, but also in all the neutral world as well. This was hard to swallow, but I did not think it would be worth while to offer anything less. I mentioned the idea to Dr. Ringer, and he seemed to receive it favorably.

When we resumed discussion the following day, he said that the plan was attractive in some ways but seemed to involve too much financial risk for his company. The largest source of income from the processes, he thought, would be the United States. Germany was not at war with the United States and did not expect to be, and he felt that I.G. was entitled to continue to receive its share of whatever could be earned from these processes in the United States—whereas I had proposed that I.G. relinquish its full interest to Standard. On the other hand, he said, the prospects for future revenue from the countries other than the United States might not be proportionate. If the proposed trade were made, therefore, he felt that I.G. was entitled to something in addition to the exchange of patent rights in the various countries.

Ringer may, or may not, have known at the time, however, something I did not learn until the following year—the Nazi government had already made a synthetic rubber agreement of some kind with the Italian government. Since Ringer had, during our first day together, mentioned that he expected soon to go to Moscow for technical discussions with the Russians, whom we both knew to be interested in Buna rubber, it is possible, also, that he foresaw the prospect of being required by his government to make some arrangements with Russia concerning Buna. Ringer recognized that Standard's minority interest in the synthetic rubber processes outside Germany was creating difficult problems for the I.G. with their own government. Apparently because of this embarrassment, I.G. had not yet asked its government for permission to include these Buna assignments in the batch he was delivering, although he freely acknowledged their obligation to do so, and promised that this would be taken care of at once.

Discussions along these lines, however, seemed to get nowhere. Ringer was unwilling to gamble on my proposed trade. I was unwilling to suggest a cash purchase. The impasse was finally broken when we agreed that what we both wanted, fundamentally, was to dissolve the joint arrangement by dividing the assets on a basis which would be absolutely fair as judged by the original contract. We decided, therefore, to adopt my plan with the provision that both parties would stand ready to review how the trade had worked out in actual operation, and, if it appeared to have been inequitable, the inequity would be adjusted in some fair way. We had come to a point, where if we were to get out of the stalemate, each of us would have to rely on the fairness and commercial integrity of the other to redress any inequitable result of this hasty division of the property.

We wrote out in longhand the "Hague Agreement" which resulted from this discussion at the offices of Standard's Dutch subsidiary company in The Hague and typewritten copies were made from the handwritten draft. The agreement was to become effective only if ratified by our respective companies. By this document the entire ownership of the Joint American Study Company—with all its "Jasco" processes—for use in the United States, the British and French empires, was to come into the hands of Standard. Standard in turn surrendered to the I.G. all of its own interest and that of the Joint Company in all these processes for the remainder of the world. Iraq was named initially as part of Standard's territory because it was a protectorate of England and therefore, arguably, a part of the British Empire, but we conceded this minor point later. Perhaps because the agreement was prepared in hand-written drafts, it was short and simple. It is reproduced in the appendix.*

Dr. Ringer mentioned to me at The Hague that through telegraphic exchanges between New York and Berlin, he understood Standard had purchased the I.G.'s holdings of 20 per cent of the stock of our patent management company, Standard-I.G. Company. On my return to London on September 26th, I obtained further information on this transaction.

On the outbreak of the war, the Standard executives in New York had become concerned about having I.G. continue as a shareholder in the Standard-I.G. Company. This was of no great financial consequence, since the shares carried only a small dividend right, ($2200 per annum) all the remaining earnings being paid out as royalties. But continued ownership of the shares gave I.G. the right to elect two of the ten directors. This would permit I.G. to keep in touch with everything done concerning these important processes throughout the

* Appendix, p. 265.

world, and thus the jointly owned patent management company would be acting as a continuing source of information for Germany. If America should itself come into the war against Germany, the I.G. stock would be seized and perhaps sold to speculators who could be of no help to the company but would be entitled to elect two of its directors. Standard's Board had therefore decided to try to purchase the I.G. stock at once, and their cabled offer of $20,000, the original cost and reasonable value of the stock, had been accepted by I.G.

With the purchase of the Standard-I.G. stock already consummated in New York, with formal assignments of all the patents covering the processes which belonged to us in hand or on their way to us, and with a plan for the territorial division of the Joint Study Company's assets and the incidental acquisition of I.G.'s stock in that company worked out, it seemed to us in London that everything had been completed which needed to be done to eliminate the I.G. as participants in the actual handling of the new processes. They would retain their royalty rights in the oil processes, but in the chemical processes all rights in the U.S., England and France would now belong to us.

These changes had been effected without making any cash payments to Germany save for the $20,000 paid for the Standard-I.G. Company stock. There had been no time to draft the lengthy contracts, which ordinarily marked each major step in the relations of these large corporations. But these hasty and skeletonized arrangements, like a typical "modus vivendi" of diplomatic usage, were adequate to form the working framework of a permanent new status between the parties.

Subsequent exchanges of cablegrams and letters confirmed the acceptance of the new framework by the parties, made some necessary corrections in legal forms, and clarified details such as the Buna process definition in which the exact technical language was an important part of the agreement.

Standard eventually had to make two additional payments to clear up the record title to the Jasco stock but these did not go to I.G.*

I returned to New York by seaplane from Foynes, Ireland, on October 9. On my return I reported to Mr. Farish in detail on the trip, sending copies to all of Standard's officers and directors. This report, perhaps better than anything else, recreates the atmosphere of that moment. It is reproduced in the appendix.†

* Appendix, p. 273.
† Appendix, p. 267.

CHAPTER VIII

THE MUNITIONS BOARD

For a generation, rubber had been essential to our domestic economy. With the outbreak of war in Europe rubber supply assumed a new and urgent strategical significance. The methodical studies of the Army and Navy Munitions Board in which we had been assisting since the first of 1939 were no longer to be considered merely theoretical. The supply line of natural rubber was obviously vulnerable—particularly if the slowly developing tenseness with Japan should ever come to war. All of this country's rubber might be cut off at the source by whoever controlled the Far Eastern plantations, or at sea by German submarines or by any power which controlled the western Pacific. Rubber ranked at the top of the list of strategic materials, for even at this early period it was becoming clear that rubber was essential both for the military machine and for the industrial machine on which it depended.

It required no military expert to sense the potential dangers, and as soon as I had reported to our own directors in New York I asked for an appointment with the Army and Navy Munitions Board in Washington. On October 19, 1939, Dr. Frolich, Dr. Hopkins and I saw the Board and reported that Standard was taking measures to get the Germans out of the Joint Study Company which owned the Buna processes. We found the Board fully alive to the increasing importance of the rubber situation. We discussed what to do next and it was agreed that the best way to make progress would be for Standard to follow up the discussions with the rubber companies which had been initiated at our request by ter Meer of

I.G. in late 1938 and which had now progressed to the point of laboratory and road testing by these companies of the latest grade of German Buna S rubber.

The first step was to apprise the rubber companies of the new situation and get them started on their own thinking on the national rubber problem in relation to the German Buna S.

On November 6, 1939, I wrote the five rubber companies who had displayed the most interest in Buna as follows:

> This personal and confidential letter is enclosed with a letter I am writing to you today announcing that the I. G. Farben-industrie has withdrawn completely from participation in the development of Buna rubbers in the United States. This announcement has not previously been made except in confidence to the U.S. Army and Navy Munitions Board. As you doubtless know, this Board is concerned over the country's present absolute dependence upon importations of crude rubber. At a recent conference with the Board, it was agreed that we should ask for your suggestions regarding the application of the Buna rubber development to this problem.
>
> I would therefore appreciate your considering the Buna development from this standpoint along with your consideration of the enclosed letter.

On November 8, Dr. Hopkins of Standard forwarded to the Munitions Board a short report on the Buna-S tests. It read:

Memorandum—Buna-S

The following is a brief summary of the tire tests made by rubber companies using Buna-S supplied by the I. G. Farbenindustrie as reported up to September 15th (1939).

B. F. Goodrich Company

Goodrich had difficulty in extruding the tread and therefore made tires by lamination on a drum. Three tires were made. Tests are being made of one tire in Florida but this has had only 3,300 miles service. At 1,700 miles the tire showed up 30% better than rubber, at 2,400 miles 16% better and at 3,300 miles 5.5% better.

Goodrich has spent most of its time compounding the Buna-S and they apparently wish to perfect compounding so that the tread extrudes well before doing much with tires.

Firestone Tire & Rubber Company

Firestone used the compounding formula suggested by the I.G. and built four tires without preliminary laboratory work. They had no trouble with extrusion but did have some difficulty in making a fast splice of the ends of the tread in applying it to the carcass. The four tires were put on a car and run in comparison with another car using natural rubber tires in a test carried out in Texas. After 9,100 miles the two front Buna-S tires were 6% better than rubber and the two rear Buna-S tires were 15% better than rubber. The splice opened 1 mm. after 3,000 miles but did not open more.

General Tire & Rubber Company

General built two tires using lamination rather than extrusion. One of these was tested by running 17,000 miles in California. The tire showed an advantage of 10% over natural rubber tires by measuring loss in volume. The looks of the tire indicated more than 10% advantage.

Goodyear Tire & Rubber Company

Goodyear has not done much with the sample furnished. They have made synthetic rubbers of Buna type in their own laboratories. They asked for and received only a 200-lb. sample of I.G. Buna-S. They reported trouble in handling and thought it no better than samples received two years ago. Made one tire and said it was only 80% as good as natural rubber.

U. S. Rubber Products, Inc.

U.S. has spent most of its time in laboratory experiments trying to check I.G.'s figures on elongation, abrasion, tensile strength, etc. At last report they were just ready to make a tire which they proposed to prepare by lamination.

The next step was to go back to the Munitions Board, review the whole situation in detail with them, and try to work out with their help the soundest possible plan for making immediate progress toward the establishment of a synthetic rubber industry of a type which would provide some measure of national security.

A meeting with the Board was arranged for November 15, 1939. Dr. Hopkins went with me and we tried to cover all the angles of the problem. Major James C. Browne, of the Board prepared the report of the meeting which was as follows:

November 16, 1939

Memorandum for: Colonels Rutherford, Hines, and all officers present in previous conference with Standard Oil Development Company re Buna rubber, the patent right for which this company has acquired:

Mr. Howard and Mr. Hopkins of the Standard Oil Development Company conferred with me during the afternoon of November 15th. The following others were included:

Commander Shaffer, representing the Navy, and Major Franks, to explain the provisions of the Educational Orders program and to discuss possible application of the Act to the subject at hand.

A. The Situation

For technical details and record of previous conference see file "Rubber Synthetic, Commodities Division."

The Standard Oil Development Company has acquired rights to German Buna rubbers. Since the current European war no further details are available concerning the technique of manufacturing processes and fabrication technique. Further development by this company hinges on several factors—pertinent ones are:

(1) This Company cannot afford to develop Buna S on a large scale since there is little or no commercial market. Buna S is believed to be the best known rubber substitute for tire manufacture. The price of natural rubber in normal times deters extensive development of this substitute. On the other hand, there is a commercial market for Buna N (similar to neoprene, Thiokol, Butyl X, and other high priced synthetics which have special uses—particularly in the oil resistance field.

(2) Buna S is (according to the Standard Oil Development

Company) an accepted excellent substitute for crude rubber for tires were we denied crude rubber in an emergency.

(3) No company wants to pioneer the development of Buna S on such a large scale that would be necessary to make the United States self-sufficient in respect to rubber—peacetime competition with natural rubber prevents, and the resultant burden is too much.

(4) It is believed that the major rubber companies would gladly acquire the rights and licenses to Buna N for which there is a going market.

B. The Proposition

The Standard Oil Development Company feels that if it licenses the production of Buna N to the major companies, it would benefit the national defense and that Company (Company benefits undisclosed, but obvious) to issue such licenses with the proviso that the licensed companies be required at the same time to develop Buna S. This would make no great or unusual demands on production, machinery or industrial facilities involved other than requirements for a small production and experimentation with a product which has no market potentialities until completely developed, or until so developed that production is at a price commensurate with that of crude rubber. Thus could a tire-rubber substitute be developed. The proposal involves the following companies: Goodyear; Goodrich; Du Pont; U.S. Rubber; Firestone; and Rohm & Haas. It was indicated that these companies would probably be pleased to acquire the license for Buna N but would react unfavorably to the proviso requiring the development of Buna S. A Government subsidy, guarantee, or some sort of outlet for tires fabricated from Buna S would help carry the burden and ameliorate this restrictive contractual clause. If the proposition that governmental assistance were unobtainable or untenable, it was suggested, and requested, that the War Department express an opinion whether it would be preferable from a national defense point of view to:

(1) Issue Buna N licenses to the companies individually and require them to separately devote a specified amount of research and development to Buna S or,

(2) Issue Buna N licenses to such companies as would agree to establish a joint development and experimental facility for development of Buna S.

This request was made with the view to seeking a proper approach to the problem from a rubber substitute angle, and a commitment was desired whether or not the Government was interested in assisting financially. In the event the Government could find no way to assist, the proposition of issuing licenses could and still may be developed. Regardless of the outcome of this proposal for Governmental aid the Standard Oil Development Company would, nevertheless, want to consider the interests of national defense.

C. Discussion

Mr. Howard and Dr. Hopkins were advised that—

(1) The Navy had minor interests and could not assist * [Comdr. Shaffer].

(2) No funds were available, with the possible exception of—

a. Those for development of substitutes for strategic material available to the branches and which were negligible [Mr. Howard believed that such funds were not sufficient to warrant consideration].

b. Educational Orders Appropriations [Major Franks explained the Act and it appeared that the probable application of such funds for this purpose was doubtful and remote].

c. Funds specifically appropriated by the next session of Congress for such a purpose [Mr. Howard showed minor interest in such future possibilities].

D. Conclusions

(1) It appears that the proposed development of Buna S would be in the interest of the national defense. The extent of the funds to be expended, if available or to be made available, should be made the subject of investigation by a board or other agency fully conversant with the situation and qualified from an economic and technical standpoint to determine the need for such development, and what may be behind this proposition other than the facts as here represented.

(2) That the Standard Oil Development Company appears seriously interested in the furtherance of this development by the

---

* This concise statement of the Navy's position on synthetic rubber remained essentially correct throughout the subsequent course. The Navy's interests, while vital to it, were statistically unimportant as compared with those of the Army and the civil economy.

issuance of licenses to the above-mentioned companies and desires to work with the military establishments in view of an ultimate solution to the rubber situation from the substitute angle.

(3) That the Standard Oil Development Company states that it will go ahead with its plans to issue licenses whether or not financial aid is forthcoming. However, it desires to be advised whether the War Department desires individual or collective development and experimental work with Buna S by the Companies licensed to use Buna N.

E. Recommendations

(1) That this matter be given consideration by The Assistant Secretary of War and an endeavor be made to assist in such an undertaking as proposed.

(2) That the Standard Oil Development Company be advised that in the meantime it should proceed with the proposed issuance of licenses and that it would appear to be more in the interest of all concerned to centralize efforts of the licensed companies to pool the research and development of Buna S.

(3) It is further recommended that a letter along the lines of the attached draft be forwarded by the Secretary of the Army and Navy Munitions Board to the Standard Oil Development Company.

James C. Browne,
Major, W.M.C.
Acting Chief, Commodities Division."

One passage in Major Browne's memorandum troubled me when I read it. That passage was: "It was indicated that these [rubber] companies would probably be pleased to acquire the license for Buna-N but would react unfavorably to the proviso requiring the development of Buna-S. A government subsidy, guarantee, or some sort of outlet for tires fabricated from Buna-S would help carry the burden. . . .

This seemed to me a summary of our opinion of the attitude of the rubber companies which might be interpreted to reflect unfairly on their public-spiritedness. I therefore at once wrote Colonel Hines, secretary of the board:

It is hardly fair to say that the rubber companies would "react unfavorably" to the development of Buna-S for tire purposes. They certainly all have a real interest in this possibility and a large amount of work would undoubtedly be accomplished voluntarily. On the other hand it would not be easy to get definite commitments to persevere in such work on a substantial scale unless some means of compensation, direct or indirect, were involved in the arrangement.

We hoped that means could be found to work out a Buna-S development as a voluntary commercial undertaking, preferably on a cooperative basis in the rubber industry. But this did not seem certain or rapid enough to be relied upon alone. The nub of the situation, as I saw it, was contained in my statement of November 22, 1939, to Colonel Hines: "A definite program which could be relied upon from the national defense and national economic standpoint, therefore, has to be based upon some set-up which will function whether or not the immediate commercial interest of the rubber companies remains active."

Together with the Munitions Board memorandum, I received a letter from Colonel Hines, which read as follows:

Major Browne, with whom you and Dr. Hopkins conferred yesterday afternoon, has presented to me the matter which you have proposed.

At present there appears to be no funds or authority whereby assistance could be given by the War and Navy Department, in connection with the development of Buna-S as proposed by you. However, I feel that should funds become available, their allotment for such a purpose would appear more readily applicable were this experimental work carried out through a centralized facility jointly conducted by the companies to whom Buna-N licenses had been granted. It is believed that the greatest good could be accomplished by a concerted effort rather than by individual undertakings.

The interest of you and your company in your desire to serve the national defense is greatly appreciated and I shall be glad to advise you should ways and means be found to assist the proposed development of a suitable synthetic rubber for automotive tire use.

We accepted this memorandum and letter from the Secretary of the Munitions Board as our directive for further action and proceeded immediately with licensing plans for Buna in the way indicated to be most helpful in meeting the military problem. The working out of plans for a jointly-owned centralized facility to take over the Buna-S development for the United States proved to be a slow and difficult task. It was several weeks before a complete tentative outline for such a plan could be crystallized, and the lawyers' criticisms of this first plan were so serious that we were at a loss on how to make further progress.

In the meantime the rubber companies, whom we hoped to have join us in this common enterprise, were pressing for separate and independent licenses to manufacture the specialty type Buna-N. With the outbreak of war in Europe imports from Germany had ceased, and although the amount immediately required was not more than one ton a day, it went into many highly profitable rubber specialties, for which the demand was increasing. There was in the United States a supply of Buna-N adequate for those already using it commercially only for about three months and absolutely none for new users.

It seemed unfair to the rubber companies and their customers to hold up this small but important specialty business until plans could be worked out for the fundamental but much more difficult problem of producing Buna-S rubber on a substantial scale for use in tires. But we did not want to sacrifice the major objective to the minor need. So a plan was devised to meet this situation. Standard decided to do three things. First, to design and build a plant for making butadiene from oil, in order to demonstrate at once at least one practical method of carrying out this basic process. Second, to erect a

Buna plant large enough to take care of the entire Buna-N demand if necessary, and also to serve as a pilot plant for the hoped-for much greater production of Buna-S. Third, to license any of the rubber companies wishing to do so to manufacture immediately their own small requirements of Buna-N, asking them at the same time to agree to experiment with Buna-S upon request of the government.

All three steps were undertaken promptly. The first two were wholly successful, the third only partially so. The licenses offered were purposely limited so as to be satisfactory only for the specialty business. The only hope for starting a basic synthetic rubber industry with private capital was through the cooperative route—all companies interested to unite in a single, large-scale facility. This was the plan we had all been talking over for a year. It was the plan which the Army and Navy Munitions Board had just advised us they thought best. But if Standard gave unlimited separate licenses to everyone there would be no basis left on which to establish a single concerted effort.

The royalty rate for these stop-gap licenses was therefore fixed at 7.5 cents per pound (which was about 25 per cent of the existing margin of profit in the special Buna-N rubber) and the licensee was to manufacture only for his own requirements. The way was thus kept open for a centralized facility which would get the only unlimited license, with the right to sell its product to anyone and the advantage of a much lower royalty rate suitable for tire rubber.

An outline of the proposed license was submitted to the rubber companies about the end of November, 1939.

Two of the largest companies, The Firestone Tire and Rubber Company and United States Rubber Company, accepted the proposal almost immediately. The Firestone license, effective January 1, 1940, was signed in March of that year. The U.S. Rubber Company agreed in June, 1940, to accept the license in order to have a basis for immediate technical cooperation with Standard, but with the expectation that they would obtain their immediate small requirements of Buna-N through us until such time as general cooperative plans had been further developed.

Despite efforts on both sides, it was not possible for Standard to arrive at an immediate agreement with the Goodyear and Goodrich companies. The basic reason was probably their feeling that if they accepted the stop-gap form of license they would be left in an unfavorable position for further negotiations with Standard.

The first rough plan for a cooperative company to produce synthetic rubber in the United States was outlined by Standard in January, 1940. The general basis was the formation of a joint company in which Standard would subscribe to 51 per cent of the common stock, the remainder to be offered to all rubber companies who wished to participate, in proportion to their consumption of rubber. Standard was to take care of any stock allotments to other participating companies, such as chemical concerns and other oil companies, out of its 51 per cent. It was proposed that Standard put into this company not only all of the Buna rights but also all of its Butyl rights as well, and that the other participants should put in any of their own synthetic rubber inventions. The synthetic processes which Standard was to put into the company—the Buna and Butyl processes—would be its principal assets. It was thought necessary to make certain that the rubber companies, as a group, should not control the company. They would be in the conflicting positions of sellers and buyers of the synthetic rubber which the company would produce. Standard and the other prospective stockholders would have no interest in conflict with that of the company and it seemed necessary for them to have the control.

In retrospect, it is clear that the plan was probably too broad and ambitious to be successful. Commercial rivalries in the rubber industry, which were extremely strong, would have hampered successful cooperation, and whether or not the plan really violated the anti-trust laws, it would certainly have been a target for attack—however well it might have served the national interest at the time. Our own company counsel, Mr. Edward F. Johnson, and our outside counsel, Mr. John W. Davis, to whom the matter was submitted, agreed that no program of this kind could be put into effect, even if materially modified, with any assurance that it would not be attacked under the anti-trust law. It was more than two years later, (June, 1942), when this Gordian Knot was cut by the Powers Small Business Act, Section 12 of which permitted the setting aside of the anti-trust laws when they interfered with the national defense.

With the receipt on April 2, 1940, of Mr. Davis' opinion, the idea of a cooperative synthetic rubber company to be privately financed and owned by the industrial groups most interested, which plan had seemed a possible solution of the national rubber problem, and the only one which could be undertaken immediately and without dependence upon government action, was quietly buried. The plan's inherent weakness was not Standard's initial ownership of a majority of the stock in the company, but the doubtful legality of such an association of all the competing rubber manufacturers in a single enterprise.

It seemed that any plan which might be devised to create a centralized facility to carry out the idea of the Army and Navy Munitions Board would be wrecked on this same legal rock, even if all the other difficulties could be met.

This plan for a cooperative company was the only scheme which, so far as I know, was ever considered for building up at that time (early 1940), wholly with private capital, a synthetic rubber industry directed toward the defense needs of the country, and with only the limited and indirect government assistance contemplated as possibly available under the

Army and Navy Munitions Board memo of November 16, 1939.

Standard next considered the possibility of complete cross-licensing and exchange of technical information between all interested companies but without any concentration of actual commercial business in a centralized facility, all parties to the plan being free to make and sell all products without restriction. An attempt was made to reach an agreement by suggesting that the patent rights of all the interested companies, including Standard, be pooled for licensing purposes; and that one-half of the total royalty be allocated to the basic patents contributed by Standard; and the other half divided among the other parties in proportion to the value of any of their contributions from time to time. At the time of its inception, this plan seemed to have a chance of success. Leaving this general cross-licensing plan under consideration by some of the rubber people, I departed for Europe in April, 1940, for what proved to be the last direct contact Standard had with the Germans on Buna rubber.

There were several interesting technical developments in Europe which were now active. The French chemical company, Etablissements Kuhlmann, had been in touch with Standard concerning a license to produce synthetic rubber and Vistanex in France. In England, also, the matter was becoming important. The Imperial Chemical Industries, which had bought a hydrogenation license and built a great plant in England soon after Standard acquired the German process in 1929, now wished to discuss the matter of a Vistanex license. We intended to open with them the subject of synthetic rubber in general, realizing that their interest extended not only to England but also to Canada, South Africa and Australia.

There was now also an urgent need for another meeting with representatives of I.G. to try to straighten out the tangle in which the war had left the English, Dutch, German and American group known as the Catalytic Research Associates.

The coming of the war made it more important than ever that the English, Dutch and American companies proceed with this plan for cooperation. They believed (and subsequent events confirmed their judgment) that the new catalytic oil refining processes then under development would be especially important for war use. Obviously this could not be done under the plan which the eight parties had so laboriously worked out in this country the month before the war broke out in Europe. This plan would have brought together as cooperators the English and Germans, now enemies.

There were two possible roads. We could scrap the entire plan and start over, omitting the Germans. Or Standard could give the other parties the benefit of all the patent rights and technical information on this subject that the Germans already had sold or communicated to Standard, and hold itself liable to meet whatever money claims the Germans might subsequently make against Standard. The second course was obviously better and was later agreed upon, but we could not commit ourselves to it without fixing with I.G. the financial basis of the claims they would make against us if we proceeded on that line. Most of the I.G. rights involved came under our 1929 agreement with them but there was a troublesome fringe of rights which the other parties wanted and which did not come under this agreement.

The United States was not at war with Germany, and if a conference with I.G. could be arranged with the consent of the State Department, we intended also to ask them to supply some of their detailed designs of manufacturing equipment and technique for Buna. We hoped that I.G. might obtain permission of its government to sell to us the plans for the Buna polymerization plants they had erected in Germany under the government program.

Standard also had received an interesting letter from Italy. Our correspondent, representing a well-known Italian company, claimed to have an important synthetic rubber process which he was ready to offer us. We were skeptical, but the letter could not be dismissed without investigation.

On April 3, 1940, Mr. W. C. Asbury and I sailed for Italy on what turned out to be the last trip of the *Rex*.

CHAPTER IX

EUROPE FALLS

Arriving in Italy in April, 1940, Mr. Asbury and I began our investigation of the Italian synthetic rubber offer. From the beginning there had seemed to be something mysterious about this proposal and it was not easy to secure the facts, but with the help of Standard's distributing subsidiary in Italy the whole story was eventually unearthed.

The Italians had been working on synthetic rubber since about 1935. Although based on the information contained in the I.G. Buna patents, their experimental work had been carried on, until very recently, without any direct contact with I.G. In following this course they had developed some variants of the German process for making Buna rubber which they claimed were new and important. But through their government they had recently made a secret agreement with I.G. and were already building their first commercial plant which was to follow the German designs and patents entirely. What the Italians were really proposing therefore was that Standard buy the alleged improvements which they had made in the German Buna process, but which the Italians were not going to use themselves. After digging out this whole background, Asbury and I lost all interest and proceeded at once to Switzerland.

We arrived in Basle, Switzerland, in mid-April of 1940. The I.G. representatives arrived almost at the same time, and we began our principal business discussions, which had to do with the clearing up of the Catalytic Research Associates problem. It was troublesome and complicated, and we found it necessary to refer several points back to New York by telephone and cable. In the intervals of these discussions we took care of several remaining details on Buna rubber which had arisen in connection with the patent lists and definitions implementing the Hague Agreement. We also broached our proposal to buy a set of designs for the latest type German Buna polymerization unit. Back at home plans and engineering studies were now under way for a Buna plant at our refinery in Baton Rouge, Louisiana. This was going to cost several hundred thousand dollars. We had estimated Standard might save as much as $100,000 if we could buy a complete set of German plans, but were afraid that restrictions on the export of any war-plant plans from Germany would prevent the I.G. from selling them to Standard. That proved to be the case. The I.G. representatives said there was no use in even raising the question with the German authorities.

One other point was very much on our minds. We wanted to make sure, if possible, that the Germans had not, since the outbreak of the war in Europe, made any radical changes in their Buna manufacturing processes or formulas. Direct questions were out of order, since the I.G. men could not discuss any phase of Germany's industrial war effort. But during the settlements of patent transfers and discussions of license definitions needed to implement the Hague Agreement, we obtained sufficient data to feel sure that all of the fundamentals of the Buna operation had remained unchanged. This conclusion was later fully confirmed.

The Norwegian campaign of April, 1940, was under way while Asbury and I were in Basle. The I.G. representatives were usually in contact by telephone with their offices in Germany every day and relayed to us, sometimes well in advance of general publication, the claims of German successes in the Norwegian campaign. The fact that these claims, extravagant and unbelievable to us when they were made, were later confirmed by press dispatches, cast a chill over us.

We also received at this time news of the death of Dr. Carl Bosch, the chairman * of the I.G. with whom Standard had negotiated its 1929 contract. He had never been able to adjust himself to the Nazi regime and had been in failing health and in even worse spirits for some three years. In telling us of his death, his associates in Basle said of him that he was the only man left in public life in Germany who still spoke his own mind on political questions.

Nothing could have better typified the status of the European war at this moment than the situation in Basle during these last meetings with the Germans in late April, 1940. Basle is situated on the Rhine River in the corner of Switzerland, where France and Germany meet. On the French side of the river was the Maginot Line, on the German side the Siegfried Line. Between these two lines of fortifications the railroads ran along the banks of the river. Trains had been running as usual over these lines since the outbreak of the war in September. Facing each other across this narrow No-Man's Land, France and Germany refrained from any attempt even to inconvenience each other by interrupting the regular rail service. Thus—until the opening of the Norwegian campaign a few weeks before—the European "sitzkrieg" had continued for eight months.

Certainly an atmosphere of sitzkrieg † was what Mr. Asbury and I found when we reached Paris. After having set aside the early plans of the Army's Service de Poudre to build a great high-octane military gasoline plant in France, the civil government now found itself unable to proceed as planned with its own substitute program. The time which had been lost could not be made up—instead the delays were of necessity multiplying.

---

* At the time of his death Dr. Bosch was chairman of the Aufsichsrat or Shareholders' Committee. Dr. Herman Schmitz, formerly financial director had succeeded him as head of the Vorstand or Management Board.

† Literally "sitting war"—the exact opposite of "blitzkrieg" or "lightning war."

America had now gone over almost exclusively to 100-octane gasoline for military use. England was fast approaching the same situation.* A few months later it was the British Spitfire plane, built around the Rolls-Royce engine and its 100-octane fuel, which won the Battle of Briton by the narrowest of margins—a margin which depended on the fuel. The French Air Force had not been able to use any large proportion of the new high compression engines because it did not feel secure on supplies of 100-octane fuel. It was now too late to do anything effective to change the situation.

An important item on our agenda for Paris was a negotiation on Vistanex and Buna rubber. These rubber discussions moved rapidly. Standard's French subsidiary, Standard Francaise des Petroles, was negotiating with the Establissements Kuhlmann, a large chemical concern with an able organization, which wanted to get started first on the production of Vistanex and, later on, synthetic rubber.

As the final drafts of this French rubber agreement were being prepared in Paris, the Germans invaded Holland and Belgium. During the next few days the trend and almost certain outcome of the Battle of France became clear. The defense was collapsing. The modernization and mechanization of the defending allied armies seemed to be only skin deep. Beneath this new front were old armies with much obsolete equipment. The internal difficulties, differences and delays which had come to my notice in connection with the French 100-octane gasoline program were apparently typical of much of the whole prewar defense effort of Western Europe.

It looked as though it would be too late for the United States to do anything except prepare to defend itself. But

* There was built in England a second great hydrogenation plant especially to supply 100 octane gasoline for the Air Force. The arrangements were much like those originally worked out by the French Army with Standard and Royal-Dutch-Shell.

that would certainly be necessary, and it seemed clear that our nation's accelerated but still modest program of military preparedness would have to be immeasurably strengthened and speeded up. There was nothing much that Standard's organization could do in France now. Plans had already been worked out in detail for the destruction of the essential parts of the great modern refinery on the Seine near Havre, if the Germans should threaten its capture. Soon afterward on instructions of the French Government the greater part of the stored oil products and the storage tanks themselves were destroyed. It had been arranged that the main office of our French refining company should be moved from Paris to La Baule, on the Atlantic coast, well to the south, and this had been done before I left.

My schedule had called for beginning discussions with Imperial Chemical Industries in England on a synthetic rubber agreement similar to that just negotiated in France with the Establissements Kuhlmann, but it was difficult to believe that the English would now have time to give to plans for new manufacturing enterprises. On the other hand, it seemed that there was still time to get new industrial plants built in America, if the country was ready now to act. The synthetic toluene development would have to be pushed and aviation gasoline capacity modernized and enormously increased. And there was Buna rubber to be considered. The swift collapse of France might convince America that in a world now plainly ruled by force, anything might happen, and "anything" might well include the cutting off of America's rubber supply.

I cabled Mr. Farish from Paris and on his instructions proceeded south through Spain, returning to the United States by plane from Lisbon to assist at once in the American programs, rather than continuing to England as originally planned. Mr. Asbury got to England on one of the last planes to leave Paris, and with Mr. Carlisle had preliminary talks with Imperial

Chemical Industries concerning the manufacture of Vistanex and synthetic rubber in England, but as we had foreseen, nothing could be accomplished under the existing conditions.

If anything had been needed to impress upon me the fact that modern warfare rests on advanced science embodied in industrial capacity, these last terrible days of France were enough.

In its long roster of great integrated companies, each made up of teams of able scientific research men, development engineers and manufacturing experts, America seemed to possess the world's finest organization for applying the most advanced science to the creation of new industrial capacity. If this organization could get into action quickly enough, America would be safe from the fate which had overwhelmed Europe.

CHAPTER X

THE ADVISORY COMMISSION

Dr. Hopkins and Dr. Frolich had gone again to discuss synthetic rubber with the Army and Navy Munitions Board on May 27, 1940. Two days later I arrived in New York from Lisbon by plane and found a letter from Colonel Charles Hines, of the Board in which he stated:

The Board is particularly anxious to ascertain at the earliest practicable time whether or not your X-Product (Butyl Rubber) is suitable for the production of automobile tires, both for the tread and the carcass. . . . I would suggest that you select the company best fitted to give us the results in the shortest possible time, due to the gravity of the situation abroad. I realize that in the commercial field you would normally give your product to all reputable manufacturers and not discriminate in favor of any one firm in the development of any of your products. . . . The information will be important as factual data in case any subsidy of the synthetic rubber industry is proposed or desired. . . . It is believed that you have sufficient data in reference to Buna "N" and "S" to advise us on those types.

I replied on May 31:

We are in entire agreement with your conclusion, and you may rely on us to act at once to determine the suitability of our "X" Product (Butyl rubber) in the manufacture of tires.

Three days later we made arrangements with the Firestone Tire and Rubber Company to visit our laboratories and discuss the Butyl development with us. Similar plans were made

113

with the U.S. Rubber Company soon thereafter. My letter of
June 4 to Mr. J. W. Thomas, then president of the Firestone
Company, shows the place which we hoped Butyl might take:

> From the standpoint of very large production within the short-
> est possible time, Butyl rubber is especially important. Not only
> as a commercial matter but because of its bearing on the national
> supply problem we ought therefore to move as rapidly as we pos-
> sibly can in the experimental application of Butyl rubber in tire
> manufacture. In view of this, we hope to avoid the necessity for
> negotiation of any formal contracts between your company and
> ours and proceed to cooperate on the simplest possible basis, con-
> firmed only by letter following the visit of your people.
> I very much appreciate your prompt action in arranging for
> the first visit and discussion.

The two rubber companies moved forward with speed and
efficiency on the testing of Butyl for tire purposes. No
lengthy contracts were ever drawn. Our agreement with
Firestone concerning Butyl was covered in a simple letter.
The Firestone agreement was dated June 6, and the U.S.
Rubber agreement June 18.

Butyl development in our own laboratories was still going
slowly. Our troubles were manifold, but the technical organization was optimistic—perhaps more optimistic than was warranted from a sober business standpoint. It was decided that,
despite the incomplete stage at which the Butyl development
stood, the time had come to announce it to the public.

The patent applications describing the original Butyl process and its improvements had been filed currently in the U.S.
Patent Office, beginning in 1937, but under American practice
these applications are not made public until the patents are
issued. There had therefore been as yet no general publicity
on Butyl rubber. Mr. Farish made the Butyl announcement
at Standard's annual stockholders meeting on June 4, 1940,
and it was given to the press. His statement read in part:

The Butyl Rubber is made from petroleum by processes more direct and simple than those required for the production of Buna rubber, and should be appreciably lower in cost. The German product was originally produced from limestone and coal, which were the cheap raw materials for Germany, and while in our own Buna plant now building at Baton Rouge it will be produced from oil, the process involves several steps. The Butyl rubber is more nearly a straight petroleum product and although its manufacture involves the most advanced technology, we have solved successfully the primary production problems and already have in operation a semi-commercial pilot plant at our Esso Laboratories in Bayway.

On June 5, Mr. John L. Collyer, President of the Goodrich Company, and one of the most far-sighted Americans in close contact with the rubber problem, announced that his company would immediately begin the production of synthetic rubber tires on a small scale. This was a well conceived and well executed plan to dramatize the rubber problem of the nation and to gain some practical experience with the manufacture and use of tires from synthetic rubber. Several thousand of these tires were distributed under the trade name of "Ameripol." This action was very helpful in stimulating general interest in synthetic rubber. The exact formula was not announced at the time and probably varied, but in general the "Ameripol" tire was understood to combine about 50 per cent natural rubber which was used for the carcass and 50 per cent synthetic rubber quite similar to the Buna-N types, which was used for the tread.

About the first of June, 1940, the Munitions Board took up the rubber problem with the newly organized Advisory Commission to the Council of National Defense and left with that body the direct responsibility for further action on the national rubber supply. The creation of the Advisory Commission was the first effort of the federal government to mobilize the nation's industrial forces for defense. Without clear legal status or powers in the beginning, it passed through an intermediate stage in which it was known as the Office of Production Management, and finally emerged as a full-grown center for the war control of industry under the name War Production Board.

On June 4, A. L. Viles, who had for many years been president of the Rubber Manufacturers Association, and one of the American representatives at the meetings of the International Rubber Regulation Committee, telephoned me from Washington to say that he had in preparation for Edward R. Stettinius, Jr., of the Advisory Commission, a review of the rubber industry's available and potential raw materials, with regard to both natural and synthetic rubber. We dictated by telephone to Mr. Viles' secretary a summary of our data on Buna and Butyl. On the following day, June 5, Mr. Viles finished his memorandum for Mr. Stettinius and sent me a copy. It represented a composite of views and data obtained by Mr. Viles from many sources and concluded with a suggestion that synthetic rubber production of 25,000 tons per annum was desirable.

It looked as though things were now beginning to move in Washington on synthetic rubber. On June 14, 1940, Mr. Farish and I appeared by invitation before the Senate Military Affairs Committee to discuss the nation's rubber problem. Mr. Collyer, of Goodrich and Mr. Ernest Bridgewater, head of du Pont's neoprene division, were the other witnesses. The Committee had no background on this problem, and only the surface could be scratched in this brief hearing, but we were all encouraged by their evident interest and desire to be helpful. Mr. Collyer suggested immediate production of 100 tons of synthetic rubber a day. The nearest to any concrete conclusion on how to get commercial production was some discussion of the possibility of licensing the importation of crude rubber and requiring a proportionate production of rubber within the country by each applicant for an import license.

Variants of this general plan had been widely used in foreign countries to encourage local production of gasoline substitutes, and as importers of gasoline in these countries Standard had become familiar with such plans. There were many objections to them, but they were direct and very effective in getting quick results. The Military Affairs Committee did not follow up this initial inquiry. It was two years later before Congress interested itself in the rubber problem in a serious way. In the meantime it was handled exclusively by the executive branch of the government.

The Advisory Commission of the Council of National Defense had, after the collapse of France in May, 1940, become the focal point of American hopes for speedy formulation of a preparedness program. Under the leadership of William S. Knudsen, Sydney Hillman and Mr. Stettinius, it enjoyed at the outset the complete confidence of the country. In view of the Army and Navy Munitions Board's clear understanding of the rubber problem and the obvious need for constructive action, there was every promise that the Advisory Commission would move energetically in this field. On June 11, 1940, I wrote Mr. Stettinius reviewing the background and present status of the synthetic rubber development and pointing out:

The basic fact is that the synthetic rubber development, if permitted to take a normal commercial course, will proceed in slow stages which cannot be expected to give us productive capacity in the U.S. of more than some insignificant fraction of our total rubber requirements within the next few years. If the objective is to obtain in the shortest possible time production capacity for a substantial proportion of our rubber requirements, the two indispensable conditions are (1) government financing and (2) cooperation along the broadest lines in the field of synthetic rubber manufacture and utilization between the competing units of the rubber industry and ourselves—with or without the inclusion of other interests—In our opinion, enabling legislation, removing the real or arguable cloud thrown by the anti-trust laws on any cooperation plan of this character is therefore essential.

The first government financing of synthetic rubber came nearly a year later. The necessary cooperation between Standard and the main competing units of the rubber industry was established on December 19, 1941, and the completion of necessary arrangements for the inclusion in the plan of cooperation of the other oil and chemical interests who were to be raw material suppliers followed early in February, 1942. The enabling legislation to remove the cloud thrown upon these forms of industrial cooperation by the anti-trust laws, as those laws were at the time being administered and interpreted, was not passed until June 11, 1942, two critical years later. In the meantime industry had proceeded under an agreement worked out between John Lord O'Brien, General Counsel of the O.P.M., and Attorney General Jackson on April 29, 1941. No single one of the three fundamentals—government financing, industrial cooperation, and enabling legislation to permit it—was in any important respect a controversial question. Nor can the slow rate of progress be ascribed to politics; there was no political issue involved.

To my letter of June 11, 1940, Mr. Stettinius replied the next day as follows:

Thank you for the informative analysis of the synthetic rubber situation contained in your letter of June 11, 1940. Your public spirited attitude is greatly appreciated.

Within a short time I shall ask you and the other principal producers whether you are willing to come down here and help us draw up a sound plan for the development of synthetics in connection with the defense program.

It was a very short time before the machinery of the Advisory Commission was working at full speed on the synthetic rubber problem. Mr. Stettinius asked Mr. Robert E. Wilson, then president of Pan American Petroleum Company, to come to Washington to act as petroleum expert for the Commission. In making this choice, Mr. Stettinius told me at the time that he had particularly in mind the fact that synthetic rubber might be one of the main preparedness problems devolving upon the oil industry, and that Mr. Wilson's background as a former professor of chemical engineering at M.I.T. would make him especially well equipped to handle it.

Almost immediately afterward there was set up a committee within the Advisory Commission charged with special responsibility on rubber. The chairman was Mr. Clarence Francis, then president of General Foods Corporation, who, in the organization of the Advisory Committee, was head of the division under which agricultural products, including natural rubber, were classified. In addition to Mr. Wilson, there was appointed to the Committee Dr. E. R. Weidlein, director of the Mellon Institute for Industrial Research at Pittsburgh, who was Chief of the Chemical Division of the Advisory Commission. Mr. Viles, president of the Rubber Manufacturers Association, acted as expert advisor for the committee and Mr. W. L. Finger, an experienced rubber man, was secretary. This group, created in June, 1940, to study and report upon the synthetic rubber problem in its broad aspects was probably as well qualified as any which could have been found in the United States at that time.

I wrote Mr. Wilson on June 28, 1940, on aviation gasoline and toluene defense programs in which he was interested, and mentioned rubber:

On the rubber matter, it seems to me that we have three related problems. First, the problem of immediate necessities, second, the long-range defense problem, and third, the long-range economic problem. I believe we should consider as a solution of all three problems the adoption of a program of import licensing which I have outlined roughly in the annexed memorandum. Any emergency financial requirements of this program could apparently now be met by the Reconstruction Finance Corporation. I have had some discussion of this principle with du Pont, Goodrich and U.S. Rubber companies and Mr. Farish and I mentioned it to the Senate Military Affairs Committee.

The memorandum attached to this letter gave details of a possible plan under which a synthetic rubber industry of any size fixed by the government would be immediately created by private industry through the compulsion and protection of controlled and licensed imports of natural rubber. I was still proceeding on the assumption that the aim should be a national rubber policy in which military and economic factors would be harmonized by the up-building of a permanent synthetic rubber industry within the United States, large enough to be a protection against the failure of imports and to hold natural rubber prices always at a reasonable level regardless of foreign "control plans," but not large enough to fill the entire needs of the country.

At my first session with the Francis Committee we did not make much progress. I understood Mr. Francis to have concluded that any governmental program for synthetic rubber should be restricted to 25,000 tons per annum—the figure which Mr. Viles had mentioned in his preliminary statistical review for Mr. Stettinius, and which seemed to me so inadequate that it might do more harm than good. Such a government program would tend to saturate the market for synthetic rubber as a specialty product and thus drive out of commercial production all the companies on whose initiative and development work the progress of general purpose synthetic would depend. With Mr. Farish's concurrence, I had pointed out the objections to this course both to Mr. Stettinius and to Mr. Viles, as soon as I received Mr. Viles memorandum in which it was mentioned.

It soon appeared that my differences with Mr. Francis on this point were due entirely to misunderstanding. He thought that Standard's objection to the 25,000-ton program was only a general objection to doing anything in a small way. The whole idea of a governmental program limited to 25,000 tons was, happily, abandoned in the earliest stages of the active study of this problem by the Francis Committee.

The Committee's study began with a series of hearings early in July, 1940.

All the rubber manufacturers were asked for their views on the synthetic rubber problem from their standpoint as consumers of these products. The Committee's views crystallized rapidly. In addition to the discussion of Buna possibilities, the Firestone Tire and Rubber Company had presented a preliminary report on their testing of Butyl for tires, indicating progress but no conclusion as yet as to its suitability. Standard submitted, to the Secretary of the Committee, a report on the general properties of Buna and Butyl which confirmed and supplemented previous discussions with the Committee. We reported that Buna-S had been proven to be a practical substitute for natural rubber, not perfect, but generally useful for tires and all principal products. We were not able to claim for Butyl any value for use in tires, inasmuch as the experimental program had not yet produced any satisfactory tires.

At a meeting of the Committee on July 17, 1940, a synthetic rubber production program of approximately 100,000 tons per annum was tentatively agreed upon. The succeeding two weeks were taken up with consideration by the committee, and discussions among all the interested parties, of possible plans for financing this program. The only concrete plan considered was to rebate the existing excise tax of 2.5 cents per pound on tires, on some sliding scale related to the consumption of synthetic rubber by the tire manufacturer. An example suggested was to waive the excise tax on 8 tons of tires for each ton of synthetic rubber used by the tire manufacturer. In effect, this would have given a subsidy of 20 cents per pound on the synthetic tire rubber.

On August 1, I was notified of the resumption of hearings by the Committee in a telegram from the Chairman which I

quote here because it summarizes conclusions reached up to
that date.

Aug. 1, 1940

Frank Howard, President Standard Oil Development Co.
30 Rockefeller Plaza
Definitely confirm meeting for Wednesday August seventh
ten thirty AM Room 2845 Munitions Building. Confidentially
committee considers all necessary steps should be taken to provide total capacity for synthetic rubber of one hundred thousand
tons per year and will consider at this conference suggested
methods of insuring market for this quantity. For reasons which
we will present, industry will be asked to engineer at its own
expense plans which would in its judgment represent practical
commercial units fitting into this program, making whatever arrangements may be necessary for raw materials. Plants to be
engineered should be in general accord with a feasible program
for your company alone or in cooperation with others but no
definite commitments for plant constructions will be asked at this
time. Please be prepared to indicate what size plant or plants you
would be willing to design. With this information we shall then
endeavor to develop suitable general plan. It is important that
definite action be started at this meeting. We are counting on
your full cooperation.

Clarence Francis

From this it appeared that the Francis Committee was ready
to recommend definitely a government synthetic rubber program of about 100,000 tons and that the next step would be
the allocation of separate or joint projects and the preliminary
engineering of these projects. Indications were that the main
foundation of any government program would have to be
Buna rubber. It was the only product with any real background of commercial experience. While we already had
license agreements with two of the four largest rubber manufacturers, Firestone and U.S. Rubber, we had as yet taken no
commitment in respect to unlimited licensing in the form nec-

essary for large-scale production of Buna for tire purposes. We had felt—and the Army and Navy Munitions Board had also felt—that any such general licensing policy should be coupled with some plan for a cooperative development of Buna in the rubber industry. If the legal objections could be met, cooperative commercial development was still a possibility, but through the Francis Committee the government itself had now taken the responsibility for working out the program, and the Committee wished to discuss both joint operations and separate operations by the rubber companies.

The day I received the Francis telegram, I wrote Mr. Litchfield, president of the Goodyear Tire and Rubber Company advising him that Standard was now ready to offer unlimited licenses for Buna rubber production for tire purposes on a straight percentage royalty.

As of August 1, 1940, therefore, Standard abandoned the plan to bring about general voluntary cooperation in the rubber industry on the development of Buna rubber on which it had been working since November, 1939, with the advice of the Army and Navy Munitions Board. This was done because it was felt that the Government had now undertaken the responsibility for the development of a synthetic rubber industry. Business was willing to follow the lead of the government in any course it might direct.

CHAPTER XI

THE PROBLEM COMES TO R.F.C.

The report of the Francis Committee, presented for discussion at the meeting of August 7, 1940, was perhaps the most complete and authoritative summary of the entire synthetic rubber situation which had been prepared up to that time.

It may be noted that in this comprehensive report, there was no mention of patents. All the parties were now talking about a government rubber program, and although a contrary impression was created in much of the subsequent discussion of the rubber program, no patent could, under the law then and now existing, prevent the government of the United States from manufacturing, or having others manufacture for it, anything it wants.*

The general meeting of August 7 between the Francis Committee and the industry representatives considered first the question of how the government might best proceed with the development of a large synthetic rubber industry. It then took up the question of engineering plans to be prepared as a foundation for the program and the companies which should undertake these plans. Dr. Hopkins' memorandum report of August 8, 1940, summarizes the discussions and conclusions of the meeting of August 7 as follows:

---

* *Note:* The government cannot be enjoined from patent infringement. The only recourse of a patent owner against the government is to file a suit for compensation in the Court of Claims. In 1918, by amendment of the basic statute, this right of the government was extended to protect not only the government itself but also anyone carrying out an operation for the government. The only patent problem which faces the government is how to minimize any liability for financial compensation to patent owners.

Memorandum on Francis Committee Meeting

Mr. Francis asked for an expression of choice between the following five plans:

1. Government plants owned and operated by the Government.
2. Government plants owned and leased to private industry.
3. Government contract to purchase for five-year period on competitive basis (with provision of Government capital).
4. Private operation of plants with R.F.C. finance.
5. Educational orders.

In all cases, it was to be assumed that the Government would provide an incentive. Each company represented at the meeting was asked to express its first, second and third choice. The result of the voting was as follows:

Plan	1st Choice	2nd Choice	3rd Choice	Total Votes
1	—	—	—	None
2	1	3	2	6
3	6	6	1	13
4	4	5	2	11
5	2	0	2	4

There next followed a discussion of methods of providing subsidies. The Chairman mentioned a list of ideas which had been presented to the Committee among which were protective tariff, outright Government subsidy to producers, and import licensing plan. No specific mention was made of the excise rebate idea. The Chairman expressed the thought that the import licensing plan might be the best method and no one disagreed, but there was a discussion as to whether this import license plan should be voluntary or made compulsory by law. The Chairman defined the import license plan as a requirement that every rubber manufacturer "buy or produce for use X amount of synthetic rubber in order to import Y amount of natural rubber." There was some expression of doubt that a voluntary plan would work but it was agreed that the Rubber Association would be asked to develop the possibility of a voluntary arrangement through the Federal Rubber Reserve people before the Committee decided as to whether it would recommend any import license plan.

The Chairman thought the conclusions arrived at might be summarized as follows:

1. To provide any substantial amount of synthetic rubber capacity, the Government must take some action.
2. A capacity of 100,000 tons per year is as good a figure as could be named.
3. Synthetic rubber is needed from a defense standpoint.
4. For defense purposes, companies present have indicated a willingness to engineer 108,000 tons capacity for plants to be financed substantially 100% by the Government.
5. Companies have expressed a willingness to engineer at their own expense that part of the engineering work outlined as being possible during the first two months in a memorandum furnished the group by the Committee.
6. It was assumed by all that a market is to be assured and the assurance will probably take the form of a Government license plan or by voluntary arrangement through the Federal Reserve people or some similar group.
7. The meeting brought out that capital requirements from the Government would be minimized by raw material suppliers not requiring financing.

The Chairman asked the wishes of the group regarding publicity in connection with synthetic rubber. It was agreed that releases should be made by the Committee only. Mr. Francis thought that an announcement might be made to the effect that there was a meeting and that industry had agreed to engineer plants to produce 100,000 tons. At the same time an effort should be made to correct errors in earlier publicity of the synthetic rubber problem by making it clear to the public that the rubber problem had not been fully solved, that plants could not be built over night but that real progress is being made. The Chairman mentioned specifically that he thought the publicity accompanying the announcement (of two named private companies) was misleading. In adjourning the meeting, the Chairman advised that the next step would have to be taken by the Committee and those present could expect to hear from the Committee at an early (but unspecified) date. For the present the Committee asked only that it be furnished with the power requirements (electric) of each company for synthetic rubber and where it was proposed to obtain this power; that is, from existing supplies, new construction, or outside purchase. Mr. Murphree is going to get us this information.

The figure of 108,000 tons capacity announced by the Chairman as having been agreed to be engineered by the 12 companies present was the total of the figures submitted voluntarily by the different companies. The statement which Standard filed with the Chairman at that time was that we were "ready to proceed with the engineering of a Butyl rubber project between 10,000 and 30,000 tons per annum, depending upon the kind and amount of financing and protection offered." On August 14, Mr. Francis wrote to confirm his understanding that we were proceeding at our own expense with preliminary engineering plans for a plant capable of producing 30,000 tons of synthetic rubber per year on a schedule which would permit us to present these preliminary plans not later than October 7, 1940.

"In the meantime," continued Mr. Francis, "the Committee, working with every expectation that the engineering plans will ultimately be required as a basis for actual production of synthetic rubber, is making every effort to develop the necessary plans for plant financing and/or for the assurance of a market for the product."

The work of the Francis Committee and the exchange of views among the companies cooperating with it had now resulted in the outline of a fairly concrete plan under which the government could establish an emergency synthetic rubber industry by financing plant construction in some way and guaranteeing an outlet for the product. It was beginning to be apparent to everyone, however, that no real progress could be made until the method of financing was settled. Mr. Stettinius and his deputy, Mr. William L. Batt of the Advisory Commission, realized this and had already established contacts with the Reconstruction Finance Corporation.

Mr. Jesse Jones, Federal Loan Administrator and as such the responsible head of R.F.C., had detailed the energetic Chairman of the R.F.C., Emil Schram, to look into the synthetic rubber matter. Through Mr. Francis, meetings were arranged in Washington between Mr. Schram and the companies most actively interested. With this step the work of the Francis Committee, in effect, was terminated. Mr. Francis resigned from active service with the Advisory Commission to the Council of National Defense on September 10. He advised us that Mr. Robert Stevens, who had been associated with him as Executive Assistant of his division, had agreed to accept the chairmanship of the Synthetic Rubber Committee temporarily. There was nothing for the Committee to do for the time being except to await the action of the R.F.C.

The figure of 108,000 tons capacity originally planned, on which preliminary studies were being made as agreed upon at the Francis Committee meeting of August 7, had in the meantime grown to 150,000 tons. This increase was due to the inclusion of Firestone and United States Rubber among those who would engineer plans. These companies had, in cooperation with Standard, undertaken for the Committee and the Reconstruction Finance Corporation the preparation of plans and estimates for two Buna-S rubber projects of 20,000 and 25,000 tons capacity, respectively. A condition was that Standard make estimates for the manufacture of the butadiene required.

But during the interim there had been much talk of cutting down the program rather than expanding it beyond 100,000 tons. As agreed upon with the Francis Committee, Standard had been preparing engineering studies for 30,000 tons capacity of Butyl production. We now felt it necessary to remind the Committee again that the use of Butyl rubber in tire compounds was still in the earliest experimental stage. It seemed to us that in view of the limited size of the government program, no projects should be included which had not demonstrated capacity to turn out rubber of established suitability for tires. We therefore asked the committee' permission to hold in reserve our plans for 30,000 tons Butyl production and to substitute plans for two projects for turning our 15,000 tons a year each of butadiene essential, of course, to the manufacture of Buna-S. One of these was to be located at the Baton Rouge refinery of Standard and the other at the plant of the Humble Oil and Refining Company at Baytown, Texas. The butadiene was to go to Firestone and U.S. Rubber companies. If the government program was reduced so as to result in the allocation of a total of only 20,000 tons of finished rubber capacity to the Firestone and U.S. Rubber companies, it was suggested that the two butadiene plants might be combined.

As regards the other raw material required for Buna-S rubber—styrene—we reminded the Committee that we owned the I.G. process for its manufacture and would, if requested, produce styrene by this process. Up to this time we had not assumed any responsibility for styrene supply. The U.S. Rubber Company had advised us that they were arranging for their own styrene supply with the Carbide and Carbon Chemical Company, and we had recommended to the Firestone Company that they obtain their styrene from the Dow Chemical Company. Dow had been for some years engaged in styrene production on a small commercial scale and was, we understood, willing to assume responsibility for a government-financed styrene plant.

Preliminary designs and estimates, worked out in cooperation with Standard, were supplied to the Committee by Firestone and U.S. Rubber for Buna-S rubber plants of 20,000 and 25,000 tons capacity, respectively, and by the Humble Oil and Refining Company and by Standard Oil Development Company in behalf of Standard Oil Company of Louisiana for complementary butadiene plants of 30,000 tons capacity.

On October 9, 1940, Mr. W. L. Batt, of the Advisory Commission wrote thanking us for the work which had been done and formally advised us that responsibility for the synthetic rubber program had now been taken over by the Reconstruction Finance Corporation. Mr. Schram was to be in direct charge.

Mr. Batt's letter closed the chapter for the Advisory Commission. Its work had been pursued with energy and ability. It had resulted in a general agreement between government and industry on a program of 100,000 tons of synthetic rubber; had determined the principle that the bulk of this capacity would have to be provided by government financing; had proceeded far enough to outline several possible plans for this financing; and had actually started the program by getting all of the interested companies to prepare preliminary engineering plans and estimates covering concrete projects. The plants were to be designed and built by the industry for the government corporation Rubber Reserve Company, but operated only in the national interest and not in competition with the commercial synthetic rubber industry which it was hoped and expected would thus be able to grow and develop its own market in a normal way. All this had been accomplished between the fall of France on the first of June and the first of October, 1940.

But this rate of progress was not maintained. Beneath the surface in Washington all was not well. On November 25, Mr. Stettinius wrote Mr. Jesse Jones as follows:

The Honorable Jesse Jones
Federal Loan Administrator
Washington, D. C.
Dear Mr. Jones:

There has been some question raised as to the speed with which the arrangements for the production of synthetic rubber are progressing. This is only to be expected because it may be a matter of vital importance in the defense effort. I want to take this opportunity, therefore, to make a matter of record this Division's responsibility in the program.

You will recall the unsatisfactory situation which resulted when conversations were carried on between representatives of the industry and both the R.F.C. and the Industrial Materials Division of the Defense Commission. At your request, therefore, and with the approval of the Commission, I turned the whole matter over to you for final determination. With my letter to you of October 23rd were enclosed a copy of my report to the Defense Commission, and the report of this Division's Chemical Group outlining the synthetic rubber situation. The same material was sent to the President on that date, together with the covering memorandum making it clear that the whole synthetic rubber situation had been turned over to you.

You are, of course, thoroughly familiar with these facts. However, I felt it desirable that it be perfectly clear that the Industrial Materials Division of the Defense Commission is not now considering itself responsible for developments in this matter.

Sincerely yours,
E. R. Stettinius, Jr.

Mr. Schram's decision to accept the presidency of the New York Stock Exchange and retire from the R.F.C. was made before any definite action was taken on the rubber matter, and Mr. Jesse Jones himself began active study of the question in conference with men from the rubber industry and our company.

At the first meeting with Mr. Jones and his associates in November, 1940, there were present Mr. H. C. Wiess, president of Standard's affiliated Humble Oil and Refining Company, Mr. Harvey Firestone, Jr., and myself. Mr. Jones opened the discussion with characteristic directness: "What do you think can be done for about $30,000,000?" This figure of $30,000,000 was in subsequent discussion reduced to $25,-000,000, and Mr. Jones has stated that the latter figure was the one he recommended to the President at the time. We told him we thought $25,000,000 to $30,000,000 might be just about enough, under suitable cooperative arrangements with industry, to finance the construction of four 10,000-ton Buna plants and the butadiene and styrene plants to supply them.

The 100,000-ton synthetic rubber program recommended by the Advisory Commission thus became a 40,000-ton program. The following colloquy between Senator Brewster and Mr. Batt* throws some light on this change.

Senator Brewster. In that connection, you contemplated that perhaps four or five of these companies should erect plants under various processes, probably approximating 25,000 tons each?

Mr. Batt. Yes.

The Chairman. What finally did develop in regard to the construction of these plants? Did they adopt the 100,000-ton program?

Mr. Batt. No, Senator. Mr. Jones has testified before this committee—at least he has made it perfectly clear publicly—that in discussions between him and the President that program was considered to be larger than was necessary. I don't know what happened from the time we turned that over in October until the Spring of the next year.

Senator Brewster. Can you answer this, Mr. Batt? In your discussions up to the time you delivered the matter to Mr. Jones, did he indicate his agreement with your viewpoint?

Mr. Batt. He felt that some synthetic rubber ought to be constructed, but he thought we were much too pessimistic in looking at the future as we did, and that our approach to so large a quantity in such an untried field was a rather wasteful one. You see, it was a very large gambling step we were proposing.

Senator Brewster. How much money did it involve, as you roughly estimated?

Mr. Batt. I should suppose that that 100,000 tons would have cost at least $1,000 or $1,500 a ton.

Senator Brewster. It would be $100,000,000?

Mr. Batt. At least that, and Mr. Jones thought we were rather reckless in our approach.

Senator Brewster. You understood thoroughly that Mr. Jones was not inclined to go along with your 100,000-ton recommendation?

Mr. Batt. Yes; we understood that, Senator.

Senator Brewster. And you would impersonalize the Presidency to the extent of leaving it to Mr. Jones to present what were the results of his conversations with the President?

* Part II, page 4286, Record of Senate Committee for the Investigation of the National Defense Program.

Mr. Batt. Oh, without doubt.

Senator Brewster. His recent statements seem to tend to lay the child on the President's doorstep and I thought it was a little unfortunate. The President has enough troubles, and I think we should let Mr. Jones say whether it was he or the President who really put the foot down on the 100,000 tons.

Mr. Batt. I must say I don't think it would have changed my judgment at the moment as to the finality with which the questions were viewed, as to what authority Mr. Jones had. He was a member of the Cabinet. He was a distinguished leader in Government, and if he said that we weren't going to finance 100,000 tons, that would have settled the matter so far as I was concerned."

It having been determined at the meeting between Mr. Jones, Mr. Firestone, Mr. Wiess and myself that the amount of money Mr. Jones proposed to spend would finance a maximum of about 40,000 tons of synthetic rubber production, the next question Mr. Jones wanted settled was, "Who is going to decide what kind of synthetic rubber ought to be made?"

Mr. Firestone gave the answer to this troublesome question, "Let each company make any kind it chooses, but require each one to use that rubber in its own tires."

This suggestion had in it the wisdom of Solomon. The Firestone and U.S. Rubber companies were expecting to produce Buna-S rubber. They were confident that they could make this rubber on a large scale and at a reasonable cost, and that they could turn out satisfactory tires from it. The Firestone Company had installed and put into operation a small commercial Buna plant in which they could make either Buna-N or Buna-S, and the U.S. Rubber Company had gone ahead with a Buna pilot plant.

The Goodrich and Goodyear companies were each taking different roads.* Goodrich was already producing some tires

---

* Statements filed in 1942 with the Senate Committee for the Investigation of the National Defense Program by the Goodyear and Goodrich companies and reviewing their activities in synthetic rubber are reproduced in the Appendix, p. 274-285.

made up of its own product, Ameripol—which was similar to Buna-N but the exact composition of which had not been announced. Goodyear was making a product known to be of the Buna-N type called "Chemigum." Goodyear and Goodrich were thus each proceeding entirely independently, and neither had as yet taken any Buna licenses or undertaken technical cooperation with the other or with Standard. There was also some sentiment in the rubber industry favoring large production of the du Pont product, neoprene. Standard, Firestone and U.S. Rubber were convinced that the Buna-S type was the only one which would meet all practical conditions imposed by any large-scale synthetic rubber development.

The government itself was not yet in any position to fix the synthetic rubber types to be developed. Mr. Firestone's suggestion was the only possible solution under the immediate conditions. The country's interest was in having synthetic rubber suitable for tires developed and produced on a large commercial scale at once. If some of the tire companies felt that varieties of synthetic rubber other than Buna-S were satisfactory for the contemplated large-scale use and were willing to stand responsible for its successful production on a large scale and its successful use in their own tires, they should be allowed to assume this responsibility.

Mr. Jones accepted this solution.

Discussions of details continued through several conferences which Mr. Firestone, Mr. Wiess and I had with the executives and the financial men of the R.F.C. whom Mr. Jones called in at once.

Out of these sessions there came in the late autumn of 1940 a definite plan for building four 10,000-ton Buna type plants and also plants to supply the raw materials for them. Seventy-five per cent of the direct cost of the projects was to be financed by the government and 25 per cent by private industry. The plants could be built as units of existing industrial installations and in this way much direct cost avoided.

This general plan matured quickly, but it was not until December 9, 1940, that we received the formal request of the R.F.C. for proposals pursuant to the plan. This original 40,000-ton plan was the first concrete step in the actual building of an emergency synthetic rubber industry in the United States.

It was a sound plan and we immediately began cooperation on plant design with the Firestone and U.S. Rubber companies. My report of January 6, 1941, to Standard's Executive Committee summarizes the situation at that time as follows:

The Reconstruction Finance Corporation requested that the proposals for the production of 40,000 tons per annum of synthetic rubber be made by January 15th. Our responsibilities in this connection have been as follows:

1. To offer the necessary patent licenses for the manufacture of synthetic rubber to the companies known to be interested. Drafts of these proposed licenses were mailed to the four principal rubber companies last week, the terms being those previously approved by the Committee. No reactions have yet been received.

2. To advise and assist our present licensees, Firestone and U.S. Rubber Company, in the preparation of their designs, estimates and proposals. This we have been doing to the best of our ability and we believe both companies will be in a position to act on or about the 15th of the month.

3. Partly as a matter of the assistance provided for in (2) above and partly as an independent commercial venture on our part we have been studying all possibilities for the supply of butadiene for the manufacture of rubber. An engineering review and estimate of capital and operating cost for the supply of butadiene from Baton Rouge and Baytown will be completed and ready for examination on January 9th. The representatives of the Humble company have been working with the Development Company at Bayway in preparation of this review and it is expected that Messrs. Wiess and Baker will arrive in New York either on the

9th or on Monday the 13th to participate in the final consideration of the data.

The decisions to be reached will be the following:

1. Best process and location for the manufacture of butadiene.
   Several alternatives, both as to nature of process and location
   of plant will have to be considered.
2. Price and other terms of contract.

Standard's part of the program—to provide for a butadiene
supply—was carried through on schedule. For more than a
year we had been weighing the relative advantages of all the
types of butadiene processes which we had studied. These
included (1) The original I.G. process based on acetylene;
(2) The alcohol process, one form of which was known to
be used in Russia, although no details were available; (3) The
I.G. chlorination process; (4) The straight thermal cracking
of petroleum; (5) The conversion of refinery or natural gases
to butadiene.

In the weighing of these possibilities the most important
consideration was the estimated availability of the materials
required if it should become necessary to produce on a scale
approximating the nation's (then) total rubber requirement of
600,000 tons per annum. This consideration alone seemed to
eliminate at once all the processes save the last one. Thus, the
original I.G. acetylene process depended upon electric power
in the required enormous quantities at locations where cheap
natural gas was available. There was no such combination
in the country. Similarly, it was believed that the chlorination process would fail for lack of chlorine, the alcohol process for lack of alcohol, and the oil cracking process for lack
of any surplus of oil adequate for this operation, remembering
that the yield of butadiene was only about 3 per cent of the
oil cracked.

The conclusion of our butadiene studies in December, 1940,
was, therefore, that the government's synthetic rubber program should be based primarily upon butane from natural

gas. Butylene from refinery gas was a better raw material and would be used to the extent that it might be available.

Although this survey was more intensive than that of the preceding October when we had first submitted preliminary studies and estimates at the request of the Francis Committee, the conclusion was the same except that we were now giving more weight to the possibility of using a process called catalytic dehydrogenation instead of thermal cracking for the conversion of butylene into butadiene. The principal advantage of the catalytic operation was that it produced a yield of butadiene twice as great as that obtained by thermal cracking. The principal disadvantage was that it had not yet been thoroughly tested and engineered, and there was, therefore, an element of uncertainty about it.

The time and effort spent by the technical organization of Standard and its affiliates on the rubber problem during this period were tremendous. The government appeared about ready to take the step which we had been contemplating since our contact with the Army and Navy Munitions Board in January, 1939, nearly two years previously—that is, actually building the foundations for an industry broad and strong enough to supply the country's rubber requirements in case of need. To our technical organization these foundations meant processes and plant designs which would not only work successfully but also be capable of quick expansion to indefinitely large limits.

Our work with the Firestone and U.S. Rubber companies had confirmed our conclusion that the manufacture of butadiene would be the critical factor if America's rubber supply were cut off. These two great and experienced companies, representing 40 per cent of the total tire manufacturing capacity in the United States, were confident that the Buna-S rubber would work out in the United States as it apparently already had in Germany, as a practical general substitute for natural rubber. The Buna-S type of rubber was relatively simple to polymerize if the raw materials, butadiene and styrene were of good quality, and no one had any doubts concerning America's ability to produce the rubber on any scale needed if these raw materials were supplied.

There was, certainly, an enormous amount of work to be done on the best way of using the rubber after it was made. To some extent these utilization problems would affect the exact Buna-S formula and the details of plant operation. If the Buna-S were made too tough it would have good strength and wear in the tire, but would be very hard to handle. On the other hand, even though softer and not so good on first test, it might be compounded with other materials to be nearly as strong as the tougher grades. The rubber companies were quite willing to take the responsibility for working their way through these problems fast enough to permit the substitution of synthetic for natural rubber as soon as the plants could be completed. The critical point, therefore, was the butadiene supply. Where could enough raw material be found to make a half million tons of butadiene a year in case of need, and what processes and plants could be best relied upon if such a contingency were to arise?

Although Standard had not by any means completed its butadiene studies by January 15, 1941, we had gone far enough to permit the Firestone and U.S. Rubber companies to submit their proposals in response to the R.F.C. request made on December 9, 1940.

By the end of January Standard had its figures prepared for a 15,000-18,000-ton-per-annum butadiene plant to be located at Baton Rouge, Louisiana, utilizing mainly butane as a raw material and had worked out the contracts for the sale of this butadiene in equal proportions to the Firestone and U.S. Rubber companies.

Execution of contracts to cover the necessary financial arrangements for plant construction and butadiene delivery was delayed pending further action by the R.F.C. on the Firestone and U.S. proposals. No such action came. On inquiry in Washington, I learned that the whole question of building a synthetic rubber industry of substantial size was now under re-examination. On February 21, 1941, I reported to Standard's Executive Committee:

> Mr. Schram admitted last Tuesday that the rubber program of the R.F.C. is in a state of suspended animation and that it is impossible to say when any action may be taken.

Many efforts have been made to appraise the considerations which led to this re-examination. At least as early as January, 1939, when I had first called on the Army and Navy Munitions Board, the military authorities had certainly favored government action of some kind to advance American synthetic rubber development. Everyone had accepted as essential the principle of government support if progress were to be rapid. The newly-created Advisory Committee of the Council of National Defense had placed the rubber problem on its agenda for urgent consideration. Mr. Stettinius had accepted the responsibility and acted promptly to refer it for study to an able committee. Between June and October, 1940, the committee had reviewed the entire rubber problem, and made its recommendations for a program of internal production of approximately 100,000 tons of synthetic rubber to be financed directly or indirectly by some plan for government support. It had even initiated the preparation of engineering studies by the companies who were expected to carry out the program. These companies had done the preliminary engineering work at their own expense.

The recommendations of the Francis Committee had been given to the R.F.C. with the understanding that the R.F.C. would work out a practical program for the Government financing. Pursuant to these recommendations, Mr. Schram of the R.F.C. had, at first, undertaken the task. On the eve of his retirement, Mr. Jones had immediately begun a personal study and had been the moving force in establishing a well-considered program for building a foundation for a national synthetic rubber industry. The program had been reduced to concrete form by December 1, 1940. The amount, 40,000 tons, was dictated by the financial limit of $30,000,000 (later $25,000,000) and was considerably less than that contemplated by the Francis Committee. But if this program had been carried through promptly, it would have provided, at about 40 per cent of the cost of the Francis Committee program, a foundation which could later be expanded—although it would have meant, as compared with the Francis program, a difference of perhaps 100,000 tons of synthetic rubber immediately available to the nation in case of emergency.

From a conservative viewpoint, the contraction of the program from 100,000 to 40,000 tons could be justified. And so far as the value of the program in affording a foundation for the quick building up of a far greater production was concerned, it would have been difficult to prove that the 40,000-ton program would not have been substantially as adequate as the 100,000-ton program. Probably four 10,000-ton units provided a much better basis for emergency expansion than a single 100,000-ton unit.

The point has also been made that the total of 100,000 tons of synthetic rubber capacity recommended by the Francis Committee was to be made up of both privately-financed and government-financed capacity. At the time Mr. Jones adopted the 40,000-ton government-sponsored program, he had reason to believe that privately-financed capacity would increase to about 30,000 tons so that *total* capacity would be 70,000 tons.

But the reappraisal of the situation at the end of 1940 does not seem to have been based upon differences in judgment on any of these practical details. It seems rather to have been on the fundamental question of whether the United States should at that time undertake to lay the foundations for a large synthetic rubber industry with government capital. Why was this question raised at this late date? What were the arguments made against proceeding with the original policy of the Army and Navy Munitions Board as confirmed and recommended by the Advisory Commission to the Council of National Defense?

The factual answers to these questions are not easy to find from any available records. It is possible only to conclude that, aside from the financial element, the following considerations each played a part in causing this pause for re-examination of the proposed national rubber program.

First, perhaps, was concern for the reaction of England and Holland to this proposal to found a great new protected manufacturing industry capable of competing with their natural rubber.

Second, was the fear, often expressed at this time, that if such an industry were created as an emergency measure, it would remain a permanent factor in American politics, striving always for the utmost in protection and influencing unfavorably our trade policies.

Third was that same over-confidence in our existing military and naval power which led to the tragic defeats of the early war years.

These arguments lay in the fields of international relations, of political economy and military judgment. We in Standard had no special knowledge or special right to be heard on such questions. But there was one argument, often repeated, which we knew from our industrial experience and special knowledge to be a dangerous fallacy.

This was the argument that, without any such extensive preparation as was contemplated by the Francis plan or the more modest Jones plan, the nation could build up its synthetic rubber capacity, if the need arose, in "time enough" to take care of its requirements. The fallacies in this argument included low estimates of the nation's requirements for rubber in time of war, high estimates of the effectiveness of reclaiming old rubber as a means of meeting an emergency situation, high estimates of the saving in rubber consumption which could be effected by cutting out "unnecessary" driving and other rubber-wasting practices in the civilian economy, and gross under-estimates of the length of time which would be required to create a synthetic rubber industry capable of supplying our national requirements.

Here we were dealing with facts and figures which, over a period of more than a year, had been studied and digested by the Army and Navy Munitions Board, by the Advisory Commission, by the rubber industry, and those of us in Standard who were intimately connected with the synthetic rubber developments. A pause for re-examination of these facts and figures by a fresh group of administration officials seemed a useless delay.

There were many of us who felt more and more strongly every day that some form of insurance of the nation's rubber supply was of grave importance. To say that the situation in Washington in January, 1941, was discouraging is understatement. We in Standard examined our own premises to see if our company interest in an American synthetic rubber industry as a technical accomplishment in which we had played some part, and in which we had some financial interest was at the root of our concern. Should we on this account sit still?

We decided we could not do that.

CHAPTER XII

INDECISION

When Mr. Schram decided to retire from the R.F.C., Mr. Jones had asked Mr. W. L. Clayton, then Deputy Loan Administrator, to take over some of the responsibilities for synthetic rubber within the R.F.C. On February 26, 1941, I called on Mr. Clayton to talk over the rubber problem with him. He handed me a memorandum dated February 20, 1941, summarizing data and conclusions which had been arrived at by some of the people who were then re-examining the rubber data. The essence of this memorandum was expressed in this conclusion:

It may be safely assumed therefore that we have in sight now, even if cut off at once from any further supply, a sufficient supply of rubber to carry us for three years.

This showed unmistakably the trend which the re-examination of the situation was taking.

When I reported this to Standard's president, Mr. Farish, he urged that I write Mr. Clayton and give him what we were convinced was a more complete and realistic picture and on February 27, 1941, I wrote him a five-page letter reviewing the rubber problem as we saw it.

But very soon after this Mr. Harvey Firestone, Jr., and Mr. F. B. Davis, Jr., President of the United States Rubber Company, told me that they understood the 40,000-ton program agreed upon in November, 1940, had now been definitely abandoned and that it was doubtful whether the R.F.C.

would do anything at all about synthetic rubber. Mr. Firestone and Mr. Davis, and doubtless other tire manufacturers, were continuing, however, to press the R.F.C. for some form of action at least; and on March 28, 1941, there was adopted a new "shadow plant" policy covered by a memorandum, which was handed to the rubber companies. The essential parts of the memorandum read:

* R.F.C. Shadow Plant Plan of March, 1941

The plant to be constructed should be sufficiently large to provide an annual capacity of 10,000 long tons, but be equipped at the present time to produce 2,500 long tons annually.

Based upon available information there is an adequate supply of raw materials to care for the contemplated production, therefore, no provision should be made in the proposal for the construction of plants to produce the required raw materials.

The RFC to own and finance the entire cost of the plant.

The manufacturing company is to agree to produce a minimum of 625 long tons of synthetic rubber during the first year of the lease. If requested RFC will undertake to supply the necessary amounts of raw materials for this production.

At least 50% of the synthetic rubber produced is to be used by the manufacturing company in the production of tires and tubes, but the RFC shall have the right to purchase 25% of this amount at the actual production cost should it so elect.

The plan for building and operating a complete foundation for a national synthetic rubber program, made up of four producing units of 10,000 tons each with all of the necessary raw material capacity to supply them, was now reduced, quite literally, to a shadow. Only four 2500-ton rubber plants were to be built, these units were to be run at only 25 per cent of their small capacity, and no government raw-material plants of any kind were contemplated. Since only one-half the rubber had to be of a quality for use in tires and tubes, the tire

* The memo bore no title. This title is the one under which the plan was known to Standard.

rubber to be turned out by the plants under the "shadow" program was less than one ton each per day.

None of us at Standard had any part in the discussion which led to this "shadow plant program." Since, however it was expected the plants would probably manufacture Buna rubber, and since the Buna process was assumed to belong to Standard, Mr. Clayton telephoned to ask whether we would be willing to waive all patent royalties and infringement claims arising out of this program. I assured him at once that we would make this waiver and confirmed the telephone conversation by letter on March 28, 1941. It is hardly necessary to read between the lines of this letter to sense the disappointment we felt.

I have discussed with my associates your suggestion that we waive all patent royalties and infringement claims arising out of the manufacture, use, or sale at cost of small quantities (approximately 1,250 tons total) of synthetic tire rubber for experimental purposes under the one-year program which you are now endeavoring to work out with the tire manufacturers.

You know it is our conviction that the synthetic tire rubber industry is essential to the national defense, and an important element in the postwar economy of the country. You also know that for two years we have been cooperating with the Army and Navy Munitions Board, the Council of National Defense, and the Reconstruction Finance Corporation in the successive stages of evolution of the governmental program on synthetic rubber. We are therefore committed in advance to the support of your very modest program, and we are glad to evidence our support by agreeing to your suggestion.

We have already been in contact with the National Defense Commission concerning the supply of butadiene in connection with the program.

Please call upon us if you think of any other way in which we can be of service in advancing this matter.

We were at this time in the final stages of construction at Baton Rouge of Standard's own Buna rubber plant which had been started more than a year before, in February, 1940. This plant had been designed for 5 tons per day. Intended primarily for the manufacture of the Buna-N type of specialty rubber, the only type which could be sold commercially in competition with natural rubber, the plant could also be used for the production of the tire rubber, Buna-S. We had intended it to serve—as it later did serve—as a guide and prototype for any expansion of the Buna rubber business which might result from governmental action.

Standard was also proceeding with a plant to produce its own butadiene for this Buna production. Our plans for this initial plant for producing butadiene had not crystallized until July, 1940, because of the uncertainties as to the government's synthetic rubber program, and our desire to coordinate commercial development with the national problem.

By the end of March, 1941, it seemed apparent that instead of being able to work out its own plans for butadiene production as a part of a national program, private industry would have to act on its own convictions and on its own responsibility and get ready to supply butadiene for any future government emergency program. It was therefore decided that Standard would proceed at Baton Rouge with a second and larger butadiene plant of the same type as the first, which, although started in July, of 1940, was not yet in operation. The second project was started at the end of April, 1941. Later, the government relied upon this plant as a supplier of butadiene for its own program.

Walter C. Teagle had retired from active service as chief executive of Standard Oil Company (New Jersey) on June 1, 1937, but at the request of the Board had remained as Chairman. We all felt free to consult him on important problems. I had followed with him from time to time the main lines of development of the rubber matter. When the Rubber Reserve Company on March 25, 1941, definitely abandoned the plan of proceeding with a substantial synthetic rubber pro-

gram and substituted the "shadow plant program," both Mr.
Farish and I expressed to Mr. Teagle our feeling that a mistake
had been made which might prove serious to the nation. Mr.
Teagle was at this time spending most of his time in Washington as a member of the National Defense Mediation Board.

The original Advisory Commission to the Council of National Defense had now become the Office of Production
Management, and Mr. R. R. Deupree, president of the Procter
and Gamble Company, had succeeded Mr. Francis as Chief of
the Agriculture and Forest Products Section. Mr. Teagle and
Mr. Deupree met frequently in Washington, began to com-
pare views on the rubber situation, and found that neither of
them was at all happy with its status. Mr. Teagle asked me to
see Mr. Deupree and give him my own views on the government rubber policy, which I did at once. Mr. Deupree was
obviously disturbed and I was sure he would take some action.

On April 7, 1941, there was addressed to me the following
letter, signed jointly by Mr. Deupree and Mr. Ernest W. Reid,
assistant chief of the Chemical Division of OPM.

We are aware of the fact that you have had some conversations
with the Rubber Reserve Company regarding the erection of
synthetic rubber plants and in this connection the O.P.M. desires
to obtain certain information that will be useful in considering
the possibility of our supply of natural rubber being completely
interrupted. We are aware that this may not happen but it is
desirable that some consideration be given to this eventuality.

If it is assumed that the supply of natural rubber is suddenly
stopped on a certain day, the Government would desire to establish synthetic rubber plants as quickly as possible producing a
type of rubber suitable for use in tires. We will appreciate your
giving us the following information based on your company producing a minimum of 50,000 and a maximum of 75,000 tons per
year assuming priorities on equipment.

(1) What rate of annual production of synthetic rubber could
you attain at the end of 18 months from any given date assuming
that butadiene and other raw materials were available?

(2) In order to attain full production within 18 months, will it be necessary to carry out any preliminary engineering work?

(3) If you could be in full production within 18 months, what reduction in time could be attained if the detailed engineering work was completed in advance?

(4) What approximate percentage of the total cost of the plant would be represented by the engineering expense?

(5) If possible, estimate the total cost of the plant for producing the minimum quantity mentioned.

It is realized that the answer to number 5 can only at this time be an estimate. The replies to the other four questions should receive careful consideration. It is suggested that statements as to ability should be conservative so that they can be fully relied upon in an emergency. We are making this inquiry with the knowledge and approval of the Rubber Reserve Company.

In New York we gave this matter priority over everything else, and on April 10, 1941, sent our reply. It was apparent from the questionnaire that the Office of Production Management was not satisfied that the shadow plant program of the R.F.C. was adequate insurance against a possible rubber famine and that they were trying to find some basis of agreement with the R.F.C. for additional measures. It was also apparent, however, that the only specific additional measure then under consideration was the preparation of some more engineering plans. This was the same compromise to which the Advisory Commission of the Council of National Defense had been driven in August of 1940 because it had no power or funds with which to do anything else. It looked as though the plan for a real government rubber program would move endlessly in circles unless someone or something blasted it out of this groove.

My own feeling at the time was that there were strong forces opposing establishment of any important synthetic rubber industry with government capital. These forces I took to be an inevitable reflection of sympathies and prejudices, of wishful thinking, economy and conservatism. Where the facts are known to everyone and there is plenty of time, the interplay of all such forces is normal and healthy. But I felt that few of those concerned had any first hand knowledge of the facts, and certainly there was not unlimited time.

No one of these adverse influences would have prevailed against a definite showing of national need. But from the nature of the problem the showing could not be definite. All that had to be done to throw doubt on it was to make up a new set of figures on probable rubber supply, stocks, and demand, and then make assumptions on the time required to build synthetic rubber plants—just the kind of figures which had been prepared in February of 1941 and which had apparently served to throw off the rails the program of December, 1940. These figures were honest enough. Each element in the statistical analysis of stocks, probable consumption, probable minimum supplies of natural rubber and probable time requirements to produce synthetic rubber seemed in itself within the bounds of reason. But the final effect of the whole argument was contrary to experience and common sense. It reminded me of an exasperated characterization of some European bankers once made by a distinguished Dutch friend: "The trouble with them is that they are so logical they have no common sense. They can reason from A to B to C with logic you cannot refute but when you look at A and then look at C you know that it is all nonsense." It did not seem possible that a world which in peace consumed more than a million tons a year of natural rubber could wage war on an unprecedented scale of mechanization and still get along for three years without any natural rubber save what it got out of the Brazilian jungles and without any advance preparation for the large-scale manufacture of a synthetic substitute.

There were many aspects of the question on which we in Standard could not claim to be experts. But we did think we knew a good deal about the industrial problems involved in production of synthetic rubber and its raw materials and the amount of time required to build up this new industry and get it running.

I therefore wrote Mr. Deupree on April 10, 1941, as follows:

The delays which will actually occur on material and equipment deliveries are unpredictable in spite of the assumption made that we would have priority orders. The rubber production could not always get first call on everything; planes, ships, ordnance will always have equal rights, and as to some material and equipment it seems almost certain that we will run into badly delayed deliveries as well as shortage of skilled labor for most rapid field construction.

Taking into account these three factors, I do not believe that it would be reasonable for you to accept the detailed estimates which are submitted by us and by others without making a general over-all time allowance of somewhere between six and twelve months for the actual completion of the program.

If there is any real chance that our imports of rubber may be seriously reduced within the next two years (and I believe we all feel that there is some chance of this), I urge that we proceed at once with a program for the construction of four 10,000-ton rubber plants; one to be erected by each of the major tire manufacturers (who will have the responsibility himself for swallowing his own output of rubber in salable tires) and simultaneously proceed with the necessary butadiene and styrene plants.

I am sorry to say that I believe the record of the handling of this synthetic rubber matter, up to this moment, has not been a creditable one.

It was our judgment in which the Firestone and United States Rubber Companies concurred that this 40,000-ton program represented the absolute minimum program which would meet the situation as it actually exists in the United States. If we are to meet an emergency the four large companies must know in advance how to produce synthetic rubber successfully and continuously on a large scale, and how to produce tires from this rubber commercially, each with his own formula and particular conditions. At least three processes of butadiene manufacture should be developed to give assurance of immediate successful production and ultimate lowest cost. At least two processes of styrene manufacture should be similarly developed.

No amount of preliminary "preparation" by way of paper designs or erection of empty shadow plants can completely meet these problems. If we spend the next six months working out a preliminary engineering and experimentation program, at least three months out of these six months will be net lost time, and the ultimate delay may be even worse than six months, because of the possibility of cumulative difficulties of all kinds which may come upon us in increasing numbers when we are trying to carry out an emergency rubber production program under conditions which will upset normal production in this country in countless ways.

The original idea and conclusion of all the people concerned, based on the theory that the government would finance the program in some way, was that 100,000 tons per annum of synthetic rubber capacity should have been begun last summer. Reluctance to make the large expenditure required rather than any justifiable doubt as to the necessity for such a program if safety of supply were to be assured was the cause of subsequent delay. Certainly something has been learned and some money has perhaps been saved. As against this we have incurred the danger of a real shortage of rubber, which we cannot now be sure we can prevent, and we have also handicapped ourselves by pushing the rubber program along until it conflicts even more seriously than it would have with the ship program, the plane program, and the general preparedness program. On the whole there is no doubt in my opinion that the savings accomplished by delay and more thorough engineering study have not by any means justified the losses and risks which we have already incurred by our delays and compromise.

I sincerely hope that the balancing of a set of paper promises as to when production might be obtained against estimates of how long the present supply of rubber might be stretched out will not be any longer taken as a justification for further inadequate measure. I would appreciate an opportunity to talk this matter through with anyone who has a contrary view; perhaps we could both learn something.

On April 15, I wrote substantially the same letter to Dr. E. R. Weidlein, Chief of the Chemical Division of the Office of Production Management (O.P.M.)

The country simply could not build and get into actual operation a large-scale synthetic rubber program in the estimated time of 12 to 18 months. If we had to "start from scratch," the time required, in our judgment, would be from 18 to 30 months, depending on what luck we had with all the new processes and their coordination and how much construction would be slowed down under the conditions of a two-ocean war—which we had to visualize as coinciding with our rubber famine.

On April 16, Mr. Deupree replied to my letter:

On my return to Washington I found your letter of April 10, and I must say your statement that we should make an overall time allowance somewhere between six and twelve months for the actual completion of the program is a bit disturbing. I would hope that something better could come out of it because, while we are all right for about eighteen months, we certainly would be in trouble if we had to wait thirty months for the production of a substitute for rubber.

I am seriously looking at your statement urging immediate erection of four 10,000-ton plants and, what's more important, that we produce and use the 10,000 tons for real experience. . . .

Dr. Weidlein replied a few days later "I agree with your point of view and am hopeful that we can do something constructive."

Mr. Farish and I made one further effort to get immediate and adequate action. Mr. R. L. Blaffer of Houston, Texas, an old friend and business associate of Mr. Farish, and also of Mr. Jones, had just been appointed Regional Advisor for the R.F.C. in the Texas district. In this connection, he came to New York and Washington to acquaint himself with his duties. Mr. Farish and I discussed the rubber problem with him in New York. On April 23, Mr. Farish handed him a letter which we had prepared together summarizing the dangers and necessities in this situation as we saw it and strongly urging that the original R.F.C. program for four 10,000-ton plants, with provision for full raw material supplies, be reinstated at once. Mr. Blaffer was convinced that our reasoning was sound and that the matter was of the utmost importance. He promised to review it with Mr. Jones and the other senior executives of the R.F.C. immediately.

On April 25, I again wrote Mr. Deupree to tell him that I had had an opportunity to discuss the subject of my letter to him with some of the Firestone organization. They were more optimistic than I on some factors and less optimistic on others, but their net conclusion was the same—that to establish a new synthetic rubber industry on a vast scale would be a matter of 18 to 30 months, not 12 to 18 months.

At about this time Mr. Deupree posed the question of whether it would not be wise for the government to engage at once the ablest expert it could find to supervise and direct the actual conduct of any engineering or construction program which might be undertaken with government funds in the synthetic rubber field. He asked what I thought of this plan and whether I had any suggestions to make. I wrote him on April 23 suggesting the names of two prominent industrial engineers. The first name suggested was that of Colonel Bradley Dewey. I had never met Colonel Dewey and my suggestion was based entirely upon his known qualifications as a chemical engineer of wide industrial and executive experience, well acquainted technically and commercially with the rubber industry but not financially interested in it. There were so few men who combined these qualifications that it was neither a coincidence nor the result of this suggestion that, a little more than a year later, Colonel Dewey was brought by Mr. Jeffers to the task of technical and engineering supervision of the nation's rubber program, and that he eventually succeeded Mr. Jeffers as Rubber Director.

These activities of the men on the actual firing line of the nation's prewar production effort, Mr. Deupree, Dr. Weidlein and Mr. Reid, were in part the cause of, and in part a reflection of, the increasing concern of the heads of the O.P.M. On May 5, 1941, Mr. A. I. Henderson, a New York lawyer, who was serving as a deputy director, addressed to the directors, Mr. W. S. Knudsen, Mr. J. D. Biggers and Mr. Batt, a letter which shows the state of feeling of the entire top organization of the O.P.M. Mr. Henderson's letter read as follows:

I should like to take this occasion to make my own views on synthetic rubber clear.

I believe that we should proceed immediately at Government expense to erect the plants necessary to produce a minimum of 100,000 tons of synthetic rubber a year. Very probably the amount should be greater. I think that this would be in accord with the policy which we have followed in materials such as aluminum and magnesium, and would be a reasonable precaution against an emergency which is likely to arise either through the closing or partial closing of the sea lanes from the East, or because of a shortage of shipping which will prevent the importation of rubber, even though the sea lanes remain open.

The recent proposal made by Mr. Deupree and Dr. Reid for the preparation of engineering plans for a 40,000 ton plant is merely a substitute halfway proposal, which I believe may be acceptable to those who are unwilling to approve the recommendation for the immediate construction of a large plant. I believe that it will save some time when the decision, which I believe is inevitable, to erect a large plant is taken. The proposal of the Reconstruction Finance Corporation to erect four small plants to produce not more than 2500 tons of synthetic rubber each year, is also a substitute. I have approved these proposals because I believe that they are better than nothing.

I believe that the Office of Production Management should take the position that the immediate construction of a large plant should be carried out immediately and that if action is not taken at once by the Reconstruction Finance Corporation, the proposal should be submitted to the President with a strong favorable recommendation.

On May 9, 1941 Mr. Knudsen acted. He wrote to Mr. Jones:

Attached you will find the brief in connection with the production of plants for synthetic rubber. It seems to me in the light of the situation and the data shown here that we should immediately make the decision to erect plants capable of producing 40,000 tons of synthetic rubber and holding our minds open for a few months until we have better knowledge of the engineering plans, with the idea that we may want to multiply this production to 100,000 or even 200,000 tons of synthetic rubber. It is my understanding that we are not delaying the production of these plants in case a larger amount is required by taking this position now.

This letter, Mr. Jones stated, was delivered to him personally on that same day by Mr. Deupree. Promptly upon the receipt of this final decisive recommendation from Mr. Knudsen, the R.F.C. acted to reinstate the complete 40,000-ton program of 1940.

On May 16, 1941, Mr. Deupree wrote to Dr. Frolich, Director of Standard's Chemical Research Division, who had been responsible for our chemical research program on synthetic rubber, as follows:

Office of Production Management
Social Security Bldg.

Dr. Per K. Frolich
Standard Oil Development Company
30 Rockefeller Plaza
New York

We want to investigate as quickly as possible the possibilities of our erecting and operating whatever plants are necessary for the production of approximately 40,000 tons annually of synthetic rubber. The question before us now is how we shall proceed. This has been discussed here at some length and the conclusion is reached that we should ask you and the men listed below to come to Washington to hold a meeting with us on Wednesday afternoon, May 21, at 2:30 in Room 1111, Lafayette Building (RFC Building), 811 Vermont Avenue, N.W.

Dr. Waldo Semon (Goodrich Company)
Dr. John Street (Firestone Company)
Dr. Sidney Cadwell (United States Rubber Company)
Dr. R. P. Dinsmore (Goodyear Rubber Company)
Dr. E. K. Bolton (duPont Company)
Dr. George Curme (Carbide & Carbon Company)

This meeting will be held under the auspices of the Rubber Reserve Company, a subsidiary of the Reconstruction Finance Corporation. Announcement may shortly be made of plans to erect four polymerization plants with immediate capacity of 2500 tons each. These plans can be carried out with the raw materials available under present productive capacities. What we have in mind here, as you will see, is a much larger program than this, involving the provision of additional raw material as well as polymerization capacity. . . .

Attached to this letter was a detailed memorandum which was to be the agenda for the meeting.

This letter and memorandum may be taken as establishing the fact that by May 16, 1941, the government's synthetic rubber program was back on the rails of progress. The patience and good sense of Mr. Deupree, with the backing of the heads of the O.P.M., had gotten the program headed back toward Mr. Jones' original goal of a minimum of 40,000 tons of plant capacity for the production of synthetic rubber of tire grade, with the necessary raw material plants to complete this infant industry.

At the meeting of May 21, 1941, the entire problem was reviewed from a technical aspect. It seems to have been accepted without question by this time that the government's main synthetic program would have to be based on the Buna-S rubber. Perhaps the most important point on which there was a difference of opinion was the relative merits of a single 40,000-ton plant as against four 10,000-ton plants. There was also a similar question on the raw material supply plants.

Differences of opinion on these questions grew out of the failure of some of the participants in the discussion to recognize that the major purpose of the program was not to get lowest costs but to build as quickly as possible a broad foundation on which an emergency industry could be erected. There was no doubt that one 40,000-ton plant could be erected at less cost, and that it would operate more economically than four 10,000-ton plants. But if four 10,000-ton plants were built by four companies, there would be four experienced organizations instead of one to assume the responsibility when the problem of emergency expansion arose. The same reasoning applied in the case of butadiene and styrene production. There the matter was even more important because of the wide differences of opinion as to the most desirable processes for their manufacture, especially in the case of butadiene. No one could say with certainty which of the processes for making butadiene would best suit the requirements for enormous expansion. To settle this point was one of the main objectives of the government's program.

Dr. Frolich's notes on this meeting indicate that these basic considerations were so well aired as to settle difference of opinion. There was still some feeling that the initial program should be the 100,000 tons recommended by the Advisory Commission instead of 40,000 tons, but in view of the experience which everyone present had had in trying to get even the 40,000-ton program reinstated, this point was not pressed. Mr. Deupree raised the question of engaging an engineering consultant and coordinator for the program, and mentioned that Colonel Dewey seemed well qualified, but no action was taken.

From this point, May 21, 1941, the reinstated government 40,000-ton program originally conceived in November, 1940, moved forward rapidly. The R.F.C. established a direct liaison with the O.P.M. through Dr. E. R. Weidlein. While remaining head of the Chemical Division of O.P.M., he became consultant and later the official Technical Advisor of the Rubber Reserve Company. He was familiar with everything that had gone before, having participated in the work of the Francis Committee and cooperated with Mr. Deupree in re-initiating the government program. His steady hand guided the technical phases of the government's efforts through the subsequent stormy period.

CHAPTER XIII

LAYING THE FOUNDATIONS

By an Act of Congress in January, 1932, the Reconstruction Finance Corporation had been given the authority, unprecedented in the history of governmental agencies, to create at will new corporations to act as its instruments. On June 28, 1940, it had created the Rubber Reserve Company, the broad charter powers of which included:

the buying, selling, acquiring, storing, carrying, producing, processing, manufacturing and marketing of natural raw or cured rubber, as well as related materials and substances; and the corporation shall have power to do all things incidental thereto and necessary or appropriate in connection therewith, including, but without limitation, the power to borrow and hypothecate, to adopt and use a corporate seal, to make contracts, to acquire, hold and dispose of real and personal property necessary and incident to the conduct of its business and to sue and be sued in any court of competent jurisdiction. . . .

The original operating organization of Rubber Reserve was headed by H. J. Klossner, a western banker who had long been a director of R.F.C.; Stanley T. Crossland, a young Chicagoan, who had been a bank examiner before joining R.F.C.; and Clay Johnson, one of the junior lawyers of the R.F.C. group who served as General Counsel through most of the critical period. Later Rubber Reserve recruited many able men from industry on a part time or whole-time basis. Mr. R. J. Dearborn of the Texas Company carried the principal burden on contracts and Mr. John Livingston of the Monsanto Company on chemical engineering.

As a member of the Reconstruction Finance Corporation group of companies, Rubber Reserve had at its disposal the general administrative, legal, accounting and engineering assistance of the entire group.

Within Rubber Reserve itself the heaviest administrative responsibility for laying the foundations of the synthetic rubber program fell on the executive vice president, Mr. Crossland, and fortunately for the nation he proved to be a man of great ability and unlimited energy.

What Rubber Reserve had undertaken to do was to establish immediately a new basic industry. This industry did not consist merely in the manufacture of synthetic rubber. It was made up of three separate layers, each an industry in itself.

The first of these layers was the production of raw materials for synthetic rubber, an operation with roots distributed throughout the United States in the chemical and oil industries. One of these raw materials, butadiene, had no long-established background of commercial production in this country, and there were the widest differences of opinion on how best to make it. The other principal raw material, styrene, had been produced commercially but only on a very modest scale by one manufacturer * in the United States. Here also there were differences of view as to the best methods for large-scale production.

The second layer was the actual polymerization or manufacture of the synthetic rubber itself. Here there were three groups to consider. The first was made up of Standard Oil Company (N.J.) and its two licensees in the development of the Buna-S process, the Firestone and U.S. Rubber companies. These three companies had been working together since the early part of 1940, and were already in agreement on questions of plant design and processing technique. The two other organizations making up this layer had each proceeded independently, Goodrich with the development of a product

* Dow Chemical Co.

of secret composition (which it identified as "Ameripol") but which from analysis seemed to be nearer to Buna-N than to Buna-S and Goodyear with another synthetic product similar to Buna-N which it identified as "Chemigum."

The third layer involved fabricating tires and other products out of the synthetic rubber. The rubber fabricating business had of course been built up on natural rubber. All the equipment, formulas, processes and the design of products had been based on the natural product, and the synthetic rubbers all differed not only from natural rubber, but also from one another. Now the United States, like Germany and Italy, had accepted the Buna-S type as the one most suitable for large-scale production. But while Buna-S simulated natural rubber closely enough to be substituted for it without revolutionary changes in the rubber fabricating industry, there was nevertheless an enormous amount of detailed adaptation needed.

These, then, were the three layers or sub-industries which together made up the new synthetic rubber industry. Each was in itself a complex industrial problem.

In addition there was the job of coordinating the three layers. It was not until the Baruch Committee report was issued in September, 1942, that there was any general appreciation of the difficulties involved in the synthetic rubber program. In June, 1941, the tiny Washington organization of the Rubber Reserve Company became the focal point for all these problems.

The basis of the program was that the new plants were to be designed and erected under the supervision of private industry, but owned by the Defense Plant Corporation, another subsidiary of the Reconstruction Finance Corporation. The government was to undertake no commitments as to the disposition of these plants after the war. It might continue to own them indefinitely or it might lease or sell them to private industry. The individual companies which designed and built the various plants, were as a rule to have no fixed options to buy them, but only a first right of negotiation with the government if it should elect to sell.

For operations, the plants were to be leased to the companies which built them, these companies to act as agents for the Rubber Reserve Company. The agent would perform all operations for the account and risk of the Rubber Reserve Company and subject to its direction. He was to be reimbursed for his expenditures and compensated by management fees agreed upon in advance.

This was the general pattern set for the program. But in any undertaking as vast as this one eventually became, it was occasionally necessary to vary the pattern. Some raw materials were obtained by purchase contracts rather than by erection of Government-owned plants. Some privately-owned plants, finished or under construction, were taken over by the government with special provisions for their repurchase by the original owner. Facilities to be added to existing privately-owned factories also presented special problems. But in general the basic pattern was that of government-owned plants, operated by private industry for the Rubber Reserve Company on the basis of reimbursement for costs, and as compensation a management fee fixed on a sliding scale reducing with quantity.

For the main production of synthetic rubber it had been decided in December, 1940, that the rubber companies should be responsible. This decision had been made because all the companies had not then agreed on the exact type of synthetic which should be produced and Mr. Firestone had proposed as a solution that each company be required to convert its own synthetic rubber into tires. The tires would have to meet the usual performance specifications of the government and other buyers. Therefore, indirectly, each producer would have to guarantee that his type of synthetic rubber would make satisfactory tires on a price basis comparable with that of other synthetic rubber.

The Deupree meeting of May 21, 1941, which had finally launched the Rubber Reserve Company's program indicated that all the companies were now agreed on Buna-S as the type of rubber which should be produced under the government program. Any operator of a government-owned plant could produce Buna-S rubber according to government specifications. Therefore, the production of Buna-S under the government's program might, in theory, have been opened to anyone at this time. Actually, the selection of agents to operate the government-owned plants was confined to rubber companies.

It was recognized that the coordination of production of Buna with its use in tires and other goods would be one of the most important and difficult problems in establishing the new industry. The rubber companies could do this job quickest, and there was no time to be lost.

Butadiene, the main raw material for the Buna-S, could in theory be made from coal, grain, oil or natural gas, so that all these industries and also of course the chemical industry were eligible as suppliers. Beginning with the work of the Francis Committee in the summer of 1940, companies operating in all these industries had been studying the subject. When the Rubber Reserve program for the production of butadiene was definitely launched in June, 1941, two processes were proposed by the chemical industry. The first was that of Carbide and Carbon Chemical Corporation * for production from alcohol by direct catalytic conversion in two steps. The second was a process of the Koppers Company, a refiner of coal tar, calling for hydrogenation of benzol derived from coal to produce cyclohexane and cracking of the cyclohexane to yield butadiene. The Koppers process was later abandoned, because of the increasing requirements for benzol for other purposes and Koppers Company thereupon reverted to the Carbide and Carbon alcohol process. Another chemical interest, the Celanese Company, carried through its initial stages a process

---

*A subsidiary of the Union Carbide and Carbon Company.

involving the conversion of selected fractions of natural gasoline into butadiene and a number of other chemical products. This project was also dropped so far as the national program was concerned.

In April, 1942, the Publicker Commercial Alcohol Company first announced a single step process, which had originated in Poland and was believed to be based on the Russian method, for the direct catalytic conversion of alcohol into butadiene, but this process was judged not sufficiently advanced to form a part of the basic program of Rubber Reserve. Therefore, the two-step alcohol process of the Carbide and Carbon Company became the only active chemical industry process. The plants for its operation were all built and operated for the government by Carbide and Carbon and by the Koppers Company, their licensee.

The various processes for making butadiene from oil have been referred to in earlier chapters. Of these only three became elements of the government program. The most important was for the direct catalytic conversion of refinery butylene into butadiene (the process developed by Standard). This method was used, under cross-licensing agreements, by most of the oil companies producing butadiene for Rubber Reserve Company. The second oil process was the one starting from butane. There were two versions of this, the earlier originating with the Phillips Company, and used only by it, and the later with the Houdry Process Corporation * and employed by Sun Oil Company and Standard Oil Company of California. This butane process used in its last step a copper acetate butadiene recovery method covered by one of the patents which Standard had gotten from the Germans. The third oil process was based on the direct thermal cracking of light petroleum distillates to yield 2 to 5 per cent butadiene and a wide variety of other products, liquid and gaseous, for

---

*A process development company operating in the oil industry and best known for its sponsorship of the Houdry Catalytic Cracking Process.

which outlets must be found.* Standard and its affiliates had pioneered this process and used it both in their own privately-owned plants and in two plants converted from other uses as a part of the Rubber Reserve Program. This process formed the basis of similar conversions, effected in other refineries late in 1942 as an emergency supplement to the basic program of butadiene production. It also used a copper acetate butadiene recovery system just mentioned and which had been greatly improved by Standard's technologists, Dr. C. E. Morrell and M. W. Swaney.

The production for the Rubber Reserve Company of styrene—the other raw material for Buna-S—followed a single basic pattern starting with benzene as raw material. The benzene was combined with ethylene to produce ethyl benzene, and in most cases the ethyl benzene was then dehydrogenated to yield styrene. Most of this styrene production used a catalyst developed by Standard's research laboratories. The principal styrene producers by this method were the Dow Chemical Company and the Monsanto Chemical Company. The Carbide and Carbon Chemical Company was the third large producer of styrene. It used a process which involved the oxidation of ethyl benzene to a carbinol, and dehydrated this material to obtain styrene. A small amount of ethyl benzene was also produced by the Canton Oil Refining Company in converted refinery equipment using a process developed by the Atlantic Refining Company.

In June, 1941, Rubber Reserve started negotiations with Standard and other potential butadiene suppliers. These negotiations moved rapidly, and on July 1, 1941, Standard was authorized by Defense Plant Corporation to proceed with designs for a butadiene unit of 15,000 tons capacity. This was

---

* An important variant of this third process was developed experimentally by United Gas Improvement Co. of Philadelphia in connection with gas manufacture, and later used in one plant by the Southern California Gas Co. at Los Angeles.

the first of the raw materials units to be authorized under the rubber program. In August, Carbide and Carbon Chemicals Corporation was authorized to erect a plant for the production of 10,000 tons of butadiene from alcohol, with the understanding that the 9,000,000 gallons of alcohol required would be provided by new facilities which Carbide and Carbon would erect at its own expense. Very soon after this Carbide and Carbon undertook to produce a further quantity of 9,000,000 gallons of alcohol from its existing facilities, and was thereupon authorized to increase its butadiene capacity to 20,000 tons.

The government's statistics on alcohol production and demand at this time indicated that there would be no surplus alcohol available for conversion into butadiene and the authorization for butadiene plants based on alcohol were therefore limited to new alcohol supplies.

These butadiene contracts with Standard and Carbide covered a total of 35,000 short tons of butadiene, more than enough to produce the 40,000 long tons of Buna rubber contemplated by the program. They also guaranteed the development of two new butadiene processes by two independent organizations.

It seemed apparent, however, that because these new butadiene plants were much more complex and difficult to build than the rubber polymerization plants, the latter could be completed much quicker and there would be no raw materials to supply them when they were ready to run. Standard had under construction in the summer of 1941 its second commercial butadiene unit at Baton Rouge intended to produce additional butadiene for Standard's own use eventually in making Buna-N rubber. In starting construction of this plant several months before, Standard had realized that it probably would not require the output for its own small Buna-N business during the first year or two after the plant was completed, but it had been convinced that there would have to be some national program on Buna-S rubber and that butadiene supply would be the critical factor here. It therefor offered to sell to the Rubber Reserve Company, for the year 1943, 5000 tons of production from this plant in order to help the Government Buna-S program get under way as soon as the synthetic rubber plants themselves could be built.

This offer, which was accepted, had an unfortunate secondary consequence. In accepting the offer, Rubber Reserve Company also requested Standard to suspend work on the designs for the 15,000-ton Baton Rouge butadiene plant which were already well advanced. This was done on the theory that Rubber Reserve Company might be able to obtain all the butadiene needed for the 40,000-ton program without this new plant construction and thus effect an important monetary saving. In theory the point was clear, but in practice it seemed impossible to convince everyone and keep them convinced that the 40,000-ton synthetic rubber program was not an end in itself, but had as its real purpose the development, within the quickest possible time, of processes and plant designs which could be used as the basis for great expansion of the synthetic rubber industry in case of emergency. The butylene-to-butadiene process of Standard, from which Rubber Reserve temporarily dissociated itself for reasons of economy in the latter half of 1941, later had to form, with the Carbide alcohol process, the only practical source for butadiene in large quantities and quickly enough to prevent disaster to the nation.

If Standard had, in fact, discontinued work on this butylene conversion process in September, 1941, the consequences would have been tragic. We, in Standard, could not believe that this was right, however, and continued the design work at our own expense. I sometimes suspected that the Rubber Reserve Company were sure we would do this and therefor felt they were taking no chances in suspending all government support of our butadiene development. However, that may have been, when Standard was ordered by telegraph, immediately following Pearl Harbor, to resume work on the 15,000 ton butylene conversion plant, no time had been lost. The basic designs had been completely worked out and revamped to include some valuable improvements. Standard was ready to proceed at once, and offered to the oil industry a completely engineered process for conversion of butylene to butadiene which was accepted as overcoming all the basic difficulties involved in previous processes of this character.

Chapter XIV

ESTABLISHING INDUSTRIAL COOPERATION

The original 40,000-ton program was planned, and had its foundations laid with no provision for cooperation among the companies concerned, save for the 1940 agreements between Standard and the Firestone and U.S. Rubber companies. To cooperate on technical development work it is necessary first of all to have some kind of agreement about patents. In June, 1941, the first steps were taken to reach a general understanding on patents applying to the manufacture of Buna rubber itself.

Rubber Reserve Company could have ignored all patent considerations under the government's statutory privileges, leaving patent owners to claim compensation at a later date. But the policy of the Reconstruction Finance Corporation, like that of the Army and Navy, had been, wherever possible, to try to settle patent questions as soon as they came up rather than leave them open for subsequent claims against the government. Rubber Reserve therefore raised with us the matter of a license under the Buna process for the operation of the Government's 40,000-ton program. While licenses might be obtained either by the operators of the plants or by the government itself, it seemed wisest for the government to take them through Rubber Reserve. This would avoid complicating the government's rubber program by the differences of opinion still existing between Standard and the Goodyear and Goodrich companies concerning the scope of the Buna patents.

The Firestone and U.S. Rubber licenes from Standard provided for the production of synthetic rubber of tire grade under a sliding-scale royalty of:

> 5 per cent of the sales price for the first 100,000 tons of total production by all licensees in the United States;
> 4 per cent for the next 100,000 tons;
> 3 per cent for all production over 200,000 tons.

Since it was impossible to determine in advance what the policy of the government would be on the sale of Buna-S rubber, it was agreed that in the government's contract the royalty should be based upon the cost of the rubber, not on the sales price. We proposed initially for the government contract the minimum rate of 3 per cent. We were asked what basis existed, other than the contracts with the Firestone and U.S. Rubber companies, for fixing this rate as a fair one. We offered: (1) A brief submitted after the last war by government counsel in an arbitration to determine royalties due the American Cyanamid Company for a process of making synthetic nitrogen. In the Cyanamid case, which seemed much like our own, the government had asked the arbitrator to fix a royalty of 5 per cent. (2) A case in England was cited. Under English law, the Controller of Patents may, in certain situations, fix the rates of royalty. Such a situation had recently arisen on a product very much like synthetic rubber. The royalty rate was fixed at 5 per cent. The British Controller of Patents was reported to have stated that he considered this a standard rate for all such chemical operations.

Rubber Reserve took the position that

. . . this program is presently intended to provide for the production of 40,000 tons of synthetic rubber per annum and is of an experimental and educational character to prepare the ground for a much larger program in case of need. Obviously, as long as natural rubber can be obtained, we cannot hope to put this synthetic rubber into automobile tires except at a loss. Accordingly, it is our feeling that during this experimental and educational period, your company should be willing to accept a token royalty payment. If because of increased cost of natural rubber, the utilization of synthetic rubber for commercial purposes, or through any other circumstances, it becomes possible to manufacture and market the product of these synthetic rubber plants on a commercial basis at a profit, we are prepared to give careful consideration at that time to payment of a 3% royalty on the use of your patents.*

We at once proposed to arbitrate the question, but this was not acceptable to Mr. Jones and his associates.

On October 27, 1941, a settlement was reached by Standard's acceptance of new figures proposed by the R.F.C. representatives. There was to be no royalty at all during the first year; 1 per cent the second year; 3 per cent thereafter.

Not only the basic Buna patents, which had been acquired from the Germans, but also all of Standard's own improvements in Buna rubber were to be available to the government under this agreement. But the four principal rubber companies all had some improvement patents relating to Buna-type rubbers. It was to be expected that they would continue to develop new detailed improvements all of which the government would wish to take advantage of for the national program. It was therefore desirable to obtain technical cooperation and exchange of information and improvement patents among the four leading rubber companies and Standard in order that technical progress might be promoted.

So far as Standard, Firestone and U.S. Rubber were concerned, this cooperation had been effective since early 1940. Dr. Byron M. Vanderbilt and a staff from Standard's laboratories had been working continuously on Buna rubber polymerization problems for two years and the data which these

* From a letter from Mr. W. L. Clayton, then Deputy Loan Administrator.

tests had developed had been carefully checked and supplemented by the Firestone and U.S. Rubber laboratories. But the Goodrich and Goodyear companies were still pursuing independent courses. Each was of the opinion that it required no license or technical help from Standard or from the other for the production of its own special type of synthetic rubber which it was selling commercially in small quantities. To protect its patent rights, Standard had, in fact, been forced to serve formal notice of patent infringement on both Goodyear and Goodrich and, on October 3, 1941, to bring suit against the latter in the federal courts for infringement of the Buna patents—not on any work Goodrich was doing for government, but solely on their private business in the commercial manufacture of a type of synthetic rubber called "Hycar" which was similar to and competed with Buna-N as a specialty product.

These commercial difficulties which Standard was having with the Goodyear and Goodrich Companies were well known to the Rubber Reserve Company. The latter was, of course, concerned only with the production of rubber for the government and had no direct interest in the question of whether Goodyear and Goodrich infringed Standard's patents in the production of their commercial specialty rubbers. The time had come, however, when Rubber Reserve wished for its own purposes to establish close technical cooperation among these five large companies experienced in Buna rubber manufacture. Anything which prevented this voluntary cooperation had now became of concern to the government.

Following conferences with Mr. Crossland of Rubber Reserve, I had prepared for his criticism the first outline of a proposal for such cooperation in the autumn of 1941, and he had talked with the rubber companies asking their views and suggesting a general meeting to try to settle the matter. The meeting was convened in Washington on December 15, 1941, eight days after Pearl Harbor.

When the early discussions failed to show any prospect of immediate agreement I proposed in behalf of Standard that all patent questions be submitted to a general arbitrator and that in the meantime the parties work out and operate under a complete technical cooperation agreement. This plan of proceeding at once on technical cooperation and arbitrating the patent questions was discussed at some length but finally rejected as impractical.* In the end, Mr. Crossland proposed in behalf of Rubber Reserve a new form of compromise which everyone accepted. Under this final compromise the government reduced still further its own possible royalty obligations and also emerged in a somewhat more favorable position in other respects than any of the rubber companies. The detailed agreement based on this government compromise proposal contained one very important and constructive addition. There was defined a broad field of synthetic rubber manufacture extending beyond the scope of the principal Buna patents, in which broader field the parties would also cooperate technically, and license each other and the government without any royalty payments by anyone.

Difficult to settle as the patent and royalty matters had been, they were only the necessary incidents to the technical information clauses of the agreement. Full exchange of technical information among all the companies and the government was stipulated, and detailed machinery was set up to implement this exchange. The Technical Advisor of the Rubber Reserve Company, Dr. E. R. Weidlein, of Mellon Institute, was to serve as the government's chairman of a technical committee made up of representatives of the parties. Through this committee there was to be a continuous and active joint technical control over all the processes, equipment and prod-

---

* It appeared later that Mr. John L. Collyer, President of B. F. Goodrich Company, had favored this plan but unfortunately he was not present during these discussions.

uct formulas involved in the government synthetic rubber program.

The formulation of clauses to accomplish this kind of co-operation presented real difficulties. The rubber industry had a tradition of secrecy as to the details of its formulas and technique. All manufacturers started with the same crude rubber, but whether a tire or a rubber heel was good or bad depended upon the skill of the manufacturer in compounding and treatment: A satisfactory solution was finally reached by provisions imposing stringent secrecy requirements on the men participating in the work of the committee and limiting the use of information obtained by exchange to the exact purpose of the agreement. In practice these secrecy provi-sions turned out to be burdensome, and to meet objections of the Baruch Committee the secrecy clauses were later sus-pended to expedite the enormous war program on synthetic rubber.

The cross-license and information exchange agreement on the synthetic rubber itself was completed in substance and signed as of December 19, 1941, the parties having remained in session almost continuously to accomplish this result. Rub-ber Reserve proceeded at once with negotiations on a similar agreement on the manufacture of the raw materials, first buta-diene and, as soon as this was out of the way, styrene.

The butadiene agreement presented problems so difficult that it is doubtful whether it could ever have been made under normal conditions. The problems arose from the fact that production of butadiene could be carried out by such diverse processes and in so many different industries that there was almost no common denominator. At the same time, it was necessary that everyone who could make any contribu-tion to butadiene production should be brought into direct contact with the government's program. The group which was ultimately brought together with the Rubber Reserve Company into a single agreement, called the "General Butadiene Agreement," included originally, in addition to four companies of the Standard group, fifteen other companies representing engineering, chemical, oil and rubber interests.*

Under this agreement, signed February 5, 1942, the parties undertook to make all their technical information on butadiene production available to one another through the intermediacy of the Rubber Reserve Company's Technical Advisor, but not ordinarily to exchange information directly with one another as provided in the rubber agreement. The Technical Advisor was left free to give to any of the parties such portions of the technical information obtained from any of the others as he thought might be helpful for the improvement of any particular plant or operation. The theory behind the agreement was that the parties would be pursuing essentially independent courses and that each one should be assisted in following its own course by all the information pertinent to that course which anyone had, but the parties would not be brought into any common course. A formula to meet such an objective is not easy to arrive at nor to apply, but it was the best that could be done. The principal difficulty arose from the chemical industry, which, like the rubber industry, is traditionally dependent upon secret data and special technique to maintain competitive positions. But these arm's length relations did not meet the need of the oil companies. There was no one who could effectively act as an intermediary between them. They needed direct contact with one another. The situation was finally met by creating a subgroup, made up of the oil companies only, in which there would be full and direct exchange of information, while the exchange among the other parties would be only through Rubber Reserve.

The patent clauses of the butadiene agreements were relatively easy to work out. A fee of ⅛ cent per pound of butadiene was agreed upon as covering all patent royalties and all

* List in appendix, p. 291.

technical information for operations for the account of the government, and ⅜ cent per pound for all private operations. The distribution of this royalty among all companies was to be settled by agreement.

The styrene agreement dated March 4, 1942, followed the pattern of the General Butadiene Agreement. In addition to Standard there were eight parties * to the styrene agreement. The fee including royalties and use of technical information in the case of styrene was fixed at ⅛ cent per pound of styrene sold to Rubber Reserve Company and 5 per cent of the sales price of styrene sold to others.

This set of agreements completed between December, 1941, and March, 1942, established the most complete and intimate technical liaison in the field of manufacture of synthetic rubbers based on butadiene and on the production of butadiene itself and styrene, the only basic raw materials required. In making the agreements the long list of companies concerned realized that they were exposing themselves to possible prosecution under the anti-trust laws. There was not at the time any law or known executive policy to protect them. Their sole reliance was the letter agreement of April 29, 1941, between the former Attorney General, Mr. Jackson, and the Chief Counsel of the O.P.M., Mr. John Lord O'Brien.

There was one temporary deviation from this logical pattern of industrial cooperation in which the business units of the nation having experience, organization or facilities useful for the synthetic rubber program were grouped together for the advancement of the program.

This deviation was the result of the brief appearance upon the rubber scene of Mr. Henry J. Kaiser.

On January 16, 1942, Mr. Kaiser called on us in New York to ask whether we would be willing to license and assist his organization in the working out of a complete synthetic rubber project in California. Mr. Kaiser was to arrange with

* List in appendix, p. 291.

an oil company for the necessary refinery gases and then carry through the production of butadiene and its conversion to Buna-S rubber.

I at once asked Rubber Reserve Company whether they would be willing to give Mr. Kaiser a place in their program if we undertook to supply for him the necessary technical information. The reply was that the Rubber Reserve Company had been unable to get any assurances of immediate action from anyone else in California and was willing to turn over this part of the rubber program to Mr. Kaiser if he could get the necessary technical background quickly enough.

Conferences in New York and Washington followed at once, and on January 22 Standard signed with Mr. Kaiser and his associate, the Bechtel McCone Company, a letter agreement under which we were to proceed at once in assisting the Kaiser organization to prepare its plans to make rubber. Work under this agreement began immediately and was at first pressed with the greatest energy, but ceased within a few weeks. Rubber Reserve advised me that the California oil companies had presented butadiene proposals which were satisfactory. The rubber polymerization was worked out with the rubber companies. These actions permitted the voluntary abandonment by Mr. Kaiser of his plan. We understood that he substituted for it another defense plant project for which he considered his organization to be better adapted.

CHAPTER XV

SETTING THE WAR PROGRAM

When the Japs struck in the Pacific and the nation found itself at war in two oceans, the wisdom and value of all the preliminary effort which had resulted in the 40,000-ton synthetic rubber plan became apparent. Mr. Jones immediately loaded down the companies already having commitments under the existing plan with all the additional commitments it was possible for them to assume at once. The machinery of cooperation which had been evolving for two years in the rubber, petroleum and chemical industries and which had been crystallized in the recent technical and patent agreements was now working at full speed under the direct administrative control of Mr. Klossner and Mr. Crossland and under the technical control of Dr. Weidlein.

The first expansion step gave a program of 120,000 tons of Buna rubber, 30,000 tons to be made by each of the four rubber companies by enlargement of the plants already under way. The raw material for this program was assured by increasing the commitments of the suppliers under the 40,000-ton program and by releasing the suspended order for the completion of Standard's 15,000-ton plant, and authorizing similar plants by other oil companies.

Pearl Harbor did not of course represent the exact date on which the national rubber problem was recognized as critical. The British and Dutch were still in control of the rubber-producing areas. There was still confidence in the strength of Singapore, in the British Navy, and in our own Pacific Fleet whose crippling losses were not yet generally known. The actual loss of America's rubber supplies was a piece-meal development over a period of months. Mr. Jones' first official announcement did not come until some time after Pearl Harbor and then it set a production goal of 400,000 tons. When the situation in the Pacific continued to deteriorate it was apparent that this would be inadequate.

Simultaneously with the loss of supplies, estimates of minimum rubber requirements jumped. It seemed clear that a great new industry, larger than any of us had ever envisioned, had to be built and that it would need the cooperation of hundreds of firms and thousands of individuals. How were they going to be educated and put into production fast enough?

There were two broad possibilities. The first was that everything be done from Washington by a central organization which would point out to everyone what he could do and coordinate the contributions of all into the complex fabric of a new industry. I doubted whether it was possible to do this in time.

The alternative was to create a situation under which the industrial machinery of the United States would, by its own initiative and by normal commercial incentives, begin the building of a synthetic rubber industry. Washington would in that case need only to pass upon proposals and coordinate plans.

If the second course were to be followed, some policy for a national synthetic rubber industry as a permanent part of the American economic picture would be essential. Only Congress could provide this. I thought Congress would do so. That any American would oppose legislation to prevent recurrence of the crisis which the Japanese successes in the Pacific were bringing upon us seemed to me in those days unlikely. The Army and Navy Munitions Board, the Advisory Commission of the Council of National Defense, and the Senate Military Affairs Committee had seemed to think, that as a permanent measure of national defense, and quite

independently of the crisis of the last few weeks, there ought
to be developed in the United States a real commercial synthetic rubber industry. Why was it not the logical thing at
once to fix a national rubber policy by law and thus give the
industrial machinery of the country a basis upon which to
proceed under its own power, so to speak? It was certain
that Congress would eventually interest itself in the wartime
synthetic rubber supply in any case, so it seemed to me that
there was much to be gained by asking immediately for legislation fixing a national policy on rubber.

I made a special visit to Washington to talk over this problem with Mr. Klossner, President of Rubber Reserve. He
expressed no opinion, but a day or so later he asked me to
return and talk to him and Mr. Jones about it. While Mr.
Jones was also noncommital at the time, it was nevertheless
quite clear that he opposed asking Congress to establish a
national rubber policy during the emergency and in general
opposed all commitments as to the postwar status of any of
the emergency commercial developments he was building up
through Defense Plant Corporation.

As a broad policy, this was undoubtedly wise. The R.F.C.
would have been lost had it followed any other general rule
in its ten billion dollar program of emergency plant construction. But it was unfortunate that the rubber program had to
suffer from this general policy. When Congress later approached the national rubber problem, it did so as a skeptical
critic of the acts and omissions of the administration rather
than as a collaborator.

Meanwhile Mr. Jones and Mr. Clayton were studying the
next expansion step. The question was, who could best undertake rapid future expansion and how fast could it be done?
Mr. H. C. Wiess, President of Standard's affiliate, Humble Oil
Company, and I discussed this matter with Mr. Jones and Mr.
Clayton in January, 1942. We were sure that the oil industry
could make an enormous amount of butadiene on a nominal

construction schedule of twelve to eighteen months. Actual time of completion would certainly be longer, as I had pointed out to Mr. Deupree.

There was one human factor which was very hard to estimate. Aside from Standard, only two companies in the oil industry—Shell Oil Co. and Phillips Petroleum Co.—had made any intensive study of the butadiene problem, and they had divergent views on many points. Other companies probably would not want to act blindly upon the opinions and advice of the companies which had studied the question. Each would want to make its own study of availability of raw materials, especially butane and butylene, and reach its own conclusion on what process it wanted to employ.

The obvious thing to do was to turn to the Office of the Petroleum Coordinator for help in enlisting the aid of the entire oil industry in butadiene production. The oil industry had a tradition of cooperation and self-reliance which it had established during the first World War and had maintained to a considerable degree ever since. When Mr. Harold Ickes had been appointed Petroleum Coordinator, he had built upon this tradition by calling on the industry to staff his governmental organization. He had also worked out with the industry a plan for an emergency organization of its own known as the Petroleum Industry War Council.

In January, 1942, there was, therefore, a smoothly functioning governmental organization for oil, the Office of the Petroleum Coordinator, meshing with a voluntary emergency organization of the industry itself—the Petroleum Industry War Council which consisted of some 200 executives of the petroleum industry. It held monthly meetings in Washington in the office of the Petroleum Coordinator and under the chairmanship of Mr. William S. Boyd, who was also President of the American Petroleum Institute.

At the first meeting after Pearl Harbor Mr. Boyd asked me to present to the Council a summary of the synthetic rubber situation as it related to the oil industry. The Office of Petroleum Coordinator had already been requested by Rubber Reserve Company and the Office of Production Management to look into all possibilities of butadiene supply from the oil industry. On January 12, 1942, a general meeting was held under the direction of the Refining Division of the Office of Petroleum Coordinator.

The official figure of rubber production given the oil industry at that time as a basis for its plans was 400,000 tons per year of Buna type rubber requiring butadiene as its principal raw material.

Of the methods of butadiene production based on the oil industry there were only two which seemed worthy of consideration for the main program; converting butane into butylene, and then converting the butylene to butadiene, or starting with by-product butylene and going directly to butadiene. Everyone agreed that there would be ample butane available to make butadiene for 400,000 tons, or far more than this, of rubber. The one-step process starting with butylene was simpler than the butane-to-butylene-to-butadiene process. The real question was whether sufficient supplies of by-product butylene would be available without cutting into the production of 100-octane gasoline, for which butylene was also required.

Standard had been studying this problem for two years. We were a major producer of 100-octane gasoline. We knew that sufficient butylene was available in our own refineries to carry much more than our proportionate share of the rubber program and at the same time permit us to make aviation gasoline at a relatively higher rate than the rate of the oil industry as a whole. The Shell Company had concluded that they were in a similar position. But the conclusions of these two companies were not at the time accepted generally by the oil industry. The prevailing opinion then, and for some time later, was that the oil industry's butadiene program would have to be based on butane.

The original plans of several of the largest of the oil companies were, then, based upon butane as a raw material. While one form of this operation had been proved practical, the processes for the first step—converting butane into butylene—involved expensive plants and serious operating difficulties. As the program developed, Standard was able to hasten the settlement of the early controversy by an important technical advance in catalytic cracking.

Since early 1939 Standard had been one of an international group called Catalytic Research Associates which had been negotiating for agreements and simultaneously developing several types of technically related catalytic refining processes. Standard's most important contributions to this development came, after the outbreak of war in Europe, in the perfection of a process called the "fluid catalyst process." In this process the catalyst is a fine powder admixed with moving gases and circulated through the refining apparatus like a fluid, at the enormous rate of from 30 to 50 tons per minute. In other catalytic processes the catalyst is either in lumps or grains and remains stationary or is handled by mechanical appliances.

The fluid catalyst process was very important in the manufacture of 100-octane aviation gasoline, but in the early days we thought it had to be run at low temperatures to do the job efficiently. This gave a relatively small production of butylene. Early in 1942 Standard learned how to operate the fluid catalyst process at very high temperatures—producing as good or even better yields and quality of aviation gasoline base stock, and at the same time multiplying the former yields of butylene. The process was at once welcomed by the oil industry, and became one of the major contributions to the war. The improvement came just in time to avoid very large expenditures which the oil industry would otherwise have made in plants for the dehydrogenation of

butane to yield butylene. One company held to its original
plan for the production of butadiene from butane, but all
other major units of the industry participating in the first main
program of Rubber Reserve adopted the Standard process of
producing butadiene from refinery butylenes.

The intimate relation between aviation gasoline production
and butadiene production from refinery butylene called for
the closest coordination between these two government supply programs. In addition, a third vital war problem of the
oil industry—production of synthetic toluene for the explosive
TNT—was closely related to the refinery operations by which
aviation gasoline and butadiene were produced. Toluene supply was handled by the Army Ordnance Department, and
this introduced an additional coordination problem. In its
attempt to meet the war emergencies the petroleum industry
encountered division of authority among the Petroleum Coordinator, the Reconstruction Finance Corporation, the Army
and the Office of Production Management (subsequently the
War Production Board). There is no doubt that these overlapping responsibilities made an inherently difficult problem
much worse. These were some of the factors that had made
us doubt whether the oil industry would be able to complete
its rubber program in any period which engineering estimates
would show.

In the middle of 1942 an effort was made to improve this
situation. Mr. Wayne Johnson, a New York lawyer of wide
interests and experience, happened to come into personal contact with some of these problems. He realized that serious
consequences would flow from this administrative tangle and
took it up directly with the President.

Mr. Johnson was asked to join the War Production Board
as a special liaison agent on oil industry problems, to try to
advance the projects which had become involved in these
overlapping responsibilities. He was a skilled negotiator and
administrator and did as much as any single individual could

do in such a position. Some matters, such as the emergency pipe lines of the oil industry, were handled expeditiously and effectively but it was not possible to do anything substantial to solve the rubber difficulties which had deep and widespread roots reaching far below the top lovel in each of these federal agencies.

One further step was taken in an effort to improve the administration of the rubber program. Mr. Arthur Newhall was appointed Rubber Coordinator for Mr. Donald Nelson, Chairman of the War Production Board. Mr. Newhall helped to smooth the road for everyone concerned with the relation of the rubber program to other war programs. But he lacked both the authority and the organization to take control of the rubber situation.

Part of the expansion of the Rubber Reserve Company's program immediately following Pearl Harbor was the provision for manufacture, under government auspices, of a small tonnage of the neoprene and Butyl types of synthetic rubber.

Standard had reported its invention of Butyl rubber to the Army and Navy Munitions Board in January, 1939. As a potential factor in any synthetic rubber program, Butyl had been under continuous consideration until October, 1940, when Standard had asked the Advisory Committee of the Council of National Defense for permission to hold the Butyl in reserve for the time being. This step had been taken because, in spite of the great promise which Butyl rubber seemed to hold out, it was felt that the Butyl development was too immature to be the main reliance of the nation in the war emergency. Even if the most optimistic engineering estimates were correct (and as it turned out, they were not) it was certain that Butyl was not so suitable for general purposes and especially for tires as Buna-S. The principal advantages it possessed were the easier availability of its raw material and prospective lower cost, both important, but secondary to the real question of whether it could be substituted for natural rubber in tires.

Standard had been proceeding aggressively in efforts to improve the Butyl product. Our expenditures on this program had run at the rate of $500,000 a year throughout 1940 and 1941. In June, 1941, we felt that the development work had proceeded to the point where we should experiment with production on a commercial basis. An appropriation of $2,-500,000 had therefore been made by the company for erection of the first commercial Butyl rubber plant. Located at the Baton Rouge refinery of Standard Oil Company, the plant was to have a nominal capacity of 10 tons per day. In October, 1941, the size of the plant had been doubled to a nominal rating of twenty tons per day and the appropriation increased to $4,500,000.

In January, 1942, immediately following Pearl Harbor, I wrote Mr. Klossner, president of Rubber Reserve, reporting on the status of the Butyl development. In early February Rubber Reserve decided to include Standard's Butyl plant in the government program as a minor source of rubber for special purposes, and asked that the plant capacity be again doubled to 40 tons per day or about 15,000 tons a year. On February 27, 1942, it once more increased the Butyl capacity to give a total of 30,000 tons per annum. At about the same time it was announced that the government was taking over a private project of the du Pont Company for the production of 10,000 tons per annum of neoprene in a new plant at Louisville, Ky. Rubber Reserve increased the size of this plant to 40,000 tons which was likewise intended as a supplement to its main Buna rubber supply for special needs. On July 27, the Butyl rubber program was stepped up to 132,000 tons per annum nominal rating, the hoped-for increase to be obtained by short-cut methods then under experimental test.

Here, then, was the original war program of the Rubber

Reserve Company—as summarized a little later by the Baruch Committee:

(Baruch Report)

The present plans for the production of synthetic rubber as outlined to us by the governmental agencies concerned call for the erection of the following types of plants in the United States:

(a) For the production of neoprene, eventual capacity 40,000 tons per year (in addition to a 9,000-ton plant now in operation by a private company).

(b) For the production of butyl rubber to yield 132,000 tons per year.

(c) For an over-all production of 705,000 tons of Buna-S. This production of Buna-S involves construction in terms of plants for producing styrene and butadiene and for the copolymerization of butadiene and styrene with the formation of Buna-S.

For the manufacture of butadiene the following processes are scheduled (all figures expressed in the long-ton equivalent of Buna-S):

	Tons
(1) From alcohol by the Carbide & Carbon Chemical process, rated capacity	242,000
(2) From butane (in natural gas) by a process developed by the Phillips Petroleum Co.	50,000
(3) From butane by the Houdry process	16,500
(4) From butylene (obtained by the cracking of petroleum) by a process developed by Standard Oil of New Jersey	283,000
(5) By the cracking at high temperatures of gas and heavy oils (the so-called thermal or refinery conversion processes)	20,000
(6) By combination of (4) and (5) in 1 locality	93,500

CHAPTER XVI

CONTROVERSY

The plan to create a national synthetic rubber industry had been evolving since 1940. There had been many delays and the program originally agreed upon between industry and the government had been greatly reduced; but good foundations had actually been laid just before Pearl Harbor, and in the months immediately afterward the expansion of the program to take care of a world almost without natural rubber had been well planned and promptly started. It was a sound program. But in early 1942 it ran into a fire of public controversy hot enough to burn out the foundations of public confidence.

The rubber controversy of 1942 was the result of the simultaneous pressure of many unrelated forces acting on a mass psychology which was at the moment highly inflammable. Defeat, humiliation and danger faced America on every foreign front. It was evident that the nation was almost wholly unprepared for the realities of the war. Following a committee hearing on one of the rubber inquiries in Washington during these days, Senator Herring of Iowa described public feeling as follows:

I never saw anything like the letters I am getting from home now, and my colleagues tell me the same story. People just want me to raise hell with somebody—it doesn't make any difference what it is about.

Among the forces and influences which reacted upon this inflammable state of public opinion to destroy confidence in the rubber program were a lively campaign by the Anti-Trust Division of the Department of Justice against Standard Oil, General Electric, Aluminum Co. of America, du Pont, Dow and many other business institutions and a series of highly publicized investigations by Congressional committees.

The American Anti-Trust laws and the legal procedure under which they are interpreted are without parallel anywhere in the world. They are distinctly an American institution, made up of a blend of solid common-law principles which we inherited from England, with a firm but as yet undefined national philosophy favoring small business. The American anti-trust law is therefore less a law than it is a national policy, the handling of which is committed to the care of the courts and to the Federal Department of Justice under the most general legislative sanctions.

To the more conservative elements of the nation's bar, the actual administration of these sanctions under our American crusading habits sometimes has the appearance of a series of legal ambuscades. A favorite scene for these controversies in recent years has been the shadowland between the patent laws and the anti-trust laws. It is apparent that the two are to be reconciled only by understanding on both sides. On the one hand the nation wishes to encourage the creation of new industries. No nation has ever found any fairer or more effective way of doing this than through patents. We promise to the one who invents or discovers the foundation for some new or improved industry that if, instead of keeping his invention a secret, he will fully disclose it to the world in a formal written document deposited in the patent office, he will have exclusive rights in it for a limited period. This promise is kept by granting a patent, which is nothing more or less than a government contract for a business monopoly for a seventeen-year period. But on the other hand, the nation abhors business monopolies. Through the instrumentality of the anti-trust laws, we commit to the Department of Justice the responsibility for destroying them on sight if it can get the courts to agree. It is not strange that conflicts develop between those who hold patents and those who enforce the anti-trust laws.

Between 1924 and 1931 Standard and several other oil companies had been through a most complex and vigorously contested anti-trust battle waged in the shadowland between the patent and the anti-trust law. The oil companies had emerged victorious with a unanimous decision of the Supreme Court, written by the liberal leader Mr. Justice Brandeis. The court found nothing contrary to law or to the public interest in a patent licensing and cross-licensing arrangement of the most complex character, covering virtually an entire industry and relating to newly patented processes of producing synthetic gasoline or "cracked gasoline." But the Anti-Trust Division of the Department of Justice had not become reconciled to the decision in this case. With a new Supreme Court and a new administration, it began several other suits involving the same legal questions, and was encouraged by new decisions. In April, 1941, it again got around to Standard and began a complete investigation of our patent contracts.

The actual investigation was concluded in February, 1942. During this period of nearly a year, the representatives of the Department examined, with the cooperation of the company, records extending over fifteen years—some 250,000 pages ranging from the minutes of the Board of Directors to the most informal pencilled memoranda of junior employees. Some 50,000 pages of these documents were photographed and sent to Washington.

Late in 1941 it seemed that excerpts made from these photographic copies were being supplied to writers and news commentators in Washington. The quotations thus publicized did not give a true picture of any phase of the business of the company. They were isolated fragments which could be made to appear as a support of sensational charges and criticism.

None of this publicity had any official connection with the anti-trust controversy. The legal position of the Anti-Trust Division was clear and proper. They challenged as contrary to the Anti-Trust Laws several of Standard's patent contracts, especially those with the I.G. Farbenindustrie. Discussions of this question were begun in late 1941 and continued through the first months of 1942.

Standard's organization, like that of other key units of industry in the United States, was at this time under great strain. In these early months of the war every phase of oil operations from the drilling of wells through the running of pipe lines, tank cars, ships, refineries and distribution terminals had its own acute problems. The central technical organization, Standard Oil Development Company, which had most of the responsibility for the questions involved in the anti-trust dispute, was perhaps the hardest hit of all. The prospective demand for 100-octane gasoline, far greater than anyone had forecast in earlier years, could not be met by the existing methods. New processes and equipment had to be worked out by Development's engineers and the plants built at the same time. The great plant which Standard's Texas affiliate, the Humble Company, had built to produce synthetic toluene for the manufacture of the basic explosive TNT was running well, but still giving the Army Ordnance Department and our own engineers the most acute concern every time it suffered from the "children's diseases" of pioneer industrial operations. Unless this new industry went satisfactorily, the allied nations would not need their proposed great new fleets of bombers— there would be no bombs for them to drop. New toluene plants were therefor already being designed for other oil refineries while the troubles in the first plant were being overcome and everyone who knew anything about this new toluene industry had to accept this assignment.

In synthetic rubber these first months of the war had brought all of the processes for which Standard was responsi-

ble to a crisis at once. The Buna-S itself had to be turned out
in the largest possible quantity as soon as possible in our small
Baton Rouge plant to provide enough material for the fabricating tests needed to help the tire plants prepare for synthetic rubber. The new butadiene process which was to form
the principal basis for the oil industry's butadiene program
was being engineered on the slimest possible basis of laboratory tests and we were trying hard to get better checks on
these data. The Butyl pilot plant, on which all Standard's
hopes for development of an immediately successful manufacturing process for this new rubber depended, was not
behaving consistently. Sundays usually found a tired group
of chemists, engineers and executives from New York assembled in the Bayway refinery for a post-mortem study of the
records of pilot runs which had come to a premature end
during the preceding week. This was a fair cross section of
the whole of American industry, big business and small business, in those critical months of 1942.

There was one more load which, for practical reasons, had
to be carried mainly by a few of the large industrial organizations. That was to serve as an emergency technical arm for
the Army and Navy. These services had only small research
and development groups of their own. So by direct contracts
and through the hastily improvised National Defense Research
Committee (and later the Office of Scientific Research and
Development) the great industrial research organizations of
the country had been loaded down with military scientific
development projects. Much of this work could be done only
by the largest and most experienced technical groups. Standard's main tasks were to develop the uses of petroleum in
offensive and defensive warfare for fog machines, flame
throwers and incendiary bombs—and to help on the super-
secret atomic bomb project, which could not then be disclosed even to the Anti-Trust Division of the Department of
Justice. Mr. R. P. Russell, the second man of Standard's tech-

nical organization, headed the "Petroleum Warfare" development program, and Mr. E. V. Murphree, the third man, became chairman of the "S-1" Planning Board which was at this time directing the atomic bomb program for the government.*

It was hard to believe that under these conditions it could serve the interests of the nation, for many of the leaders of these teams of scientists and engineers to appear in courts all over the land to defend prewar patent and research agreements which lay at the roots of many of their new developments.

In the first World War a similar, although not nearly so acute, situation had arisen and, by agreement of the cabinet officers concerned, anti-trust prosecutions had been virtually suspended for the period of the war.

Eventually this same solution had to be adopted in 1942, under persuasion from the White House. By a Presidential letter dated March 20, 1942,† it was arranged that anti-trust prosecutions were to be suspended where they interfered with war-production activities and, in instances where the departments concerned could not agree, appeal to the White House was provided. Although this decision of the President left a theoretical possibility of further anti-trust action, in reality it settled the issue. There were no more anti-trust prosecutions involving the important industrial production machinery of the nation until the end of the war.

The President's letter dated March 20, which fixed the national policy and would have postponed the whole patent-anti-trust issue until the end of the war, was not released until March 28. The release therefore came too late to affect Standard's case, which had in the meantime been settled under a voluntary "Consent Decree" on March 25.

The consent decree terminated the litigation by ending all

* Smyth Report, Sec. 5.5.
† Appendix, p. 292.

the contracts complained of without admission by any party that it had been wrong.* Mr. Leo T. Crowley had just been appointed Alien Property Custodian, and as his first official act he seized all of the German rights under these agreements and then, as legal owner of those rights, joined in the settlement by Standard.

Thus it became possible to end in a manner satisfactory both to the Anti-Trust Division and Standard a legal controversy concerning the bearing of the anti-trust laws on the handling of the monopolies created by patents which, if tried, would have been perhaps the most involved of all the controversies which have ever been waged in this legal shadowland. We were soon to learn, however, that while this prompt settlement ended Standard's legal connection with the rubber dispute, it marked only the beginning of the public controversy on rubber.

By Senate Resolution 71 of February 13, 1941, the Senate had created a Special Committee for the Investigation of the National Defense Program of which Senator Truman of Missouri was the first Chairman.

It began a series of hearings in early 1942, which were intended to explore "cartels" and their effect on the national defense. The investigation of synthetic rubber, which was undertaken by the Committee as a part of this inquiry was followed by a companion investigation by the Senate Committee on Patents, carried out in the form of hearings on two Senate Bills, 2303 and 2491, providing for rather drasitc amendments of the patent laws. The chairman of the Senate Patents Committee was Senator Bone of Washington.

In the performance of their proper functions these committees each pursued an independent course, but external forces endeavored with some success to convert the inquiries into a public investigation of Standard.

* Appendix, p. 295.

This phase began with the publication on February 11, 1942, of an open letter from the Union for Democratic Action in New York. A copy of this letter was sent to Senator Truman. It charged that "The rubber shortage which threatens to cripple America's war effort and disrupt the whole life of the American people is due in large part to the obstruction of I. G. Farben working with subsidiaries of Standard Oil of New Jersey."

At or about this time contact was established between this Committee and the Anti-Trust Division of the Department of Justice. In advance of its public hearings the Committee undertook private hearings through a sub-committee. At these private hearings the Department of Justice first presented what later became the principal theme of these two inquiries —the "cartel" theory.

The opening statement of the Assistant Attorney General, Mr. Thurman Arnold, before the full committee was made on March 26, 1942, the day after the settlement of the anti-trust suit. It summarized the cartel theory as follows:

The shortage in synthetic rubber due to the suppression of independent experimentation, production and distribution by this cartel agreement we are about to show the Committee is in the limelight today because the consumer realizes it more than the shortage of other basic materials. Nevertheless, it is fair to the defendants to point out that there is essentially no difference between what the Standard Oil Co. of New Jersey has done in this case and what other companies did in restricting the production of magnesium, aluminum, tungsten carbide, drugs, dyestuffs, and a variety of other critical materials vital for the war. So long as such cartel agreements continue to exist, the inevitable result will be shortages in essential materials.

To establish the existence of a cartel between Standard and the I.G., Mr. Arnold cited the Division of Fields Agreement of 1929 through which Standard had obtained a minority interest in the Buna rubber process. Mr. Arnold interpreted this agreement as an effort by Standard to get I.G.'s help in monopolizing the world's oil business in return for Standard's help to I.G. in monopolizing the world's chemical business.

The opinion of the Committee on this was summarized in its report as follows:—

There is considerable evidence that the development of Buna-S type rubber, which is regarded as the best type of synthetic rubber in the United States, was seriously retarded as the result of the 1929 agreement between I. G. Farbenindustrie and Standard, and the action taken pursuant thereto. By their joint action I. G. Farbenindustrie and Standard were able to discourage independent rubber companies from entering into the independent development and production of synthetic rubber, they preferring that whatever development of synthetic rubber took place in the United States be done under license from them.

To complete the record of current official opinion, two other statements seem pertinent.

On March 7, 1942, in the midst of the controversy, General Charles Hines, U.S.A., who, as Secretary of the Army and Navy Munitions Board during the prewar years, had been cooperating with us in trying to find some way to establish a national synthetic rubber industry, wrote Dr. Per K. Frolich, Director of Standard's Chemical Research Division, as follows:

I know that you are very much interested in the current newspaper articles on the delay in the synthetic rubber production, and both you and I realize that had they taken your advice sometime ago we would have been in a much better position and from one to two years ahead of our present schedule.

On June 3, 1943, when the first great units of the new industry had just begun to turn out rubber successfully, the Rubber Director, Mr. William Jeffers, held a press conference in Houston, Texas. At this conference the Rubber Director told the newsmen:

Had it not been for the research and engineering development work carried on by Standard Oil Company of New Jersey prior to Pearl Harbor, the synthetic rubber program would be one and a half to two years behind what it is now.*

The anti-trust suit against Standard, the Congressional investigations of "cartels" and patents, and the publicity campaign which fed upon, and in turn fed some, of these official proceedings were the original sources of the cloud of misunderstanding which rose over and obscured the synthetic rubber problem in early 1942.

Controversy of this kind has a cumulative effect. When public confidence begins to wane, it is easy to accelerate the decline and very hard to stop it. A new accelerating force which had its effect during the critical months of March to July, 1942, arose from the investigation of the synthetic rubber program from a different angle by a sub-committee of the Senate Committee on Agriculture and Forestry, appointed to make "a complete study and investigation of the production of industrial alcohol, synthetic alcohol, and synthetic rubber." The chairman of this sub-committee was Senator Gillette of Iowa.

In March, 1942, stocks of wheat in the United States were 810,000,000 bushels. The grain elevators of the country were full and crops were left in the fields in some areas. The price of wheat was being maintained at $1.20 a bushel by government purchases, under the pressure of what seemed to be a permanent over-production. The grain producers felt they were in a precarious position and might find themselves drowned in unmarketable grain at any moment.

Because of the higher cost of grain, practically all natural industrial alcohol has been produced in the United States by the fermentation of molasses rather than grain, the grain being used only for alcoholic beverages. Some small amount of the

* J. H. Carmichael in the N. Y. *Times* of June 6, 1943.

molasses originated in the United States but most of it was imported from Cuba. The normal production and consumption of this industrial alcohol in the United States had been climbing slowly before the war toward a figure of about 100 million gallons per annum. With the outbreak of war in Europe, the demand for the product rose rapidly. Consumers had all been warned by the O.P.M. during the year 1941 that demand for industrial alcohol for the production of explosives might require so much of the supply that normal use for non-essential purposes would have to be reduced.

By March, 1942, another important factor was affecting the alcohol situation. That was the German submarine campaign on the Atlantic Coast. The vessels which carried oil and molasses were being sunk in sight of our shores. No one knew when this situation would be any better. With the import of molasses from Cuba seriously reduced, the supply of industrial alcohol was apparently going to drop at the very time when the demand was increased. Therefore the Rubber Reserve Company, on the advice of the O.P.M., had proceeded on the assumption that it must limit its alcohol-butadiene program to a modest proportion of the total * and rely upon direct production from petroleum for everything else.

This was the situation to which Senator Gillette's Committee directed its attention.

The first witnesses before the Committee represented a group which had been for many years endeavoring to develop a plan for the erection of small distilleries dispersed through the grain-producing areas by which grain would be converted into industrial alcohol. The new plan was that these plants should be now erected and this agricultural alcohol used instead of petroleum or synthetic alcohol from pe-

---

*Actually it had been limited to the increased production of synthetic industrial alcohol which Carbide and Carbon Chemical Company had undertaken to make.

troleum for the production of butadiene for rubber. It was also urged that the butadiene should be actually converted to rubber in small synthetic rubber plants distributed through the farm areas.

It was at once realized by many people that great harm to the country might result if the Gillette Committee's study of the rubber situation were made to appear before the public during these critical days as an issue in which industry was opposing agriculture. To assist in dispelling any such false impression and with the desire to do everything possible to hurry production of rubber from any source, Mr. Farish, then President of Standard, wrote on May 8, 1942, to the Secretary of Agriculture, Claude R. Wickard, and to Senator Gillette, as follows:

> In view of your statement today, I am writing to inquire whether this company can be of assistance to you in your consideration of the use of agricultural alcohol as a raw material for the manufacture of butadiene for rubber production.
>
> . . . . . .
>
> If it should appear that our process above referred to, or any of our other processes, would be of any value in the program of immediate production of synthetic rubber from agricultural alcohol they will be available, royalty free, for the duration of the war, and we will render all possible technical assistance in connection with the program.*

From this time Standard remained in contact with the Department of Agriculture and the Gillette Committee and, on the invitation of Senator Gillette, Mr. Farish, with Mr. Murphree and Mr. Asbury of Standard's technical staff, testified before the Committee on July 28, 1942.

Due to the good sense and patriotism of Senator Gillette and his associates the work of this Committee was never permitted to degenerate into a trial of any false issue of oil vs

* Full text of letter Appendix, p. 296.

grain—although efforts were made to head it that way. The Committee, however, did get pointed in the direction of endeavoring to establish that the production of rubber from oil would be a failure. Much testimony was adduced to the effect that none of the processes of producing butadiene from oil had been practically developed, that butadiene produced from oil would not make satisfactory rubber, and that the amount of critical material * required to build for these plants would be greater than the amount required for the production of butadiene from alcohol, even if new fermentation plants had to be built to produce the alcohol.

Unfortunately this thesis was supported by two controversies which developed within the oil industry at this time. The first controversy had to do with the availability of butylene as a raw material for the manufacture of butadiene. A number of the oil companies who had undertaken to supply butadiene for Rubber Reserve Company at first proposed to make their butadiene from butane, asserting that they had no butylene available. This seems to have been due mainly to the fact that Standard and one or two other companies, as the result of a longer and more extensive experience in the production of 100-octane gasoline than the oil industry at large, had advanced much further in increasing production and recovery of butylene and in the substitution of other refinery gases for butylene in the manufacture of 100-octane gasoline. In some refineries it was true that sufficient butylene was not available for butadiene production and also aviation gasoline production, but with the greatly expanding demands for aviation gasoline, new equipment for its manufacture was required and it had been shown that the new fluid catalyst plants which were already included in this program for 100-octane gasoline manufacture, were capable of being run to

* Material such as steel, copper, etc. of which supplies were inadequate for both military demand and civilian requirements.

produce large additional amounts of butylene without reducing aviation gasoline production.

While these matters were still under study there appeared full-page advertisements in the papers of Washington and other leading cities in which the claim was made that an entirely new process which used butane as raw material was the key to the production of butadiene from petroleum. It was asserted that the petroleum industry and the government would save time, money and critical material, if the current plans were abandoned and the new proposal substituted. The inference from these advertisements was that the responsible government officials had not been willing to take proper action on the new process and that this appeal therefore was being made directly to the public. The press sensed the news value of this situation immediately.

The Gillette Committee made some investigation of the new butane process but unfortunately instead of clarifying the matter this seemed only to confuse the entire situation. A procession of experts appeared before the Committee, giving facts, assumptions and opinions on the various possible processes and plant designs for the production of butadiene from alcohol and petroleum. Certainly there was much disagreement among them. The Committee had no staff with which to carry on scientific examinations or to reconcile or explain the inconsistent information obtained from others. The picture left in the minds of the Committee, of the press, and of the public was therefore one of endless controversy in the rubber program.

The work of the Committee did however help to clarify one very important issue—the possible availability of large new supplies of grain alcohol, and for this service the Rubber Director subsequently acknowledged the country's indebtedness to Senator Gillette.

CHAPTER XVII

CONFUSION

The threatened shortage of industrial alcohol which had existed at the end of 1941 and early in 1942 had resulted in a thorough re-examination by the newly created War Production Board * of the possibilities of increasing the supply. The work of the Gillette Committee focused attention on the great surplus of grain. As a result, a plan was worked out for converting 95 per cent of the beverage-distilling capacity of the United States to industrial alcohol production. This, of course, meant stopping the production of whiskey and gin; and required as well a certain amount of new plant construction and alterations.

But the time and critical materials involved were negligible as compared with the alternative program of producing alcohol in entirely new plants. The grain stocks of the country seemed at the time so enormous that it was difficult to believe there could be any shortage of grain for foodstuffs. Provided only the country was willing to forego the manufacture of whiskey and gin for the period of the war,† the alcohol production could be raised to 400,000,000 gallons, three times the prewar production. At the same time a grain surplus which was becoming a political and economic embarrassment could be disposed of.

Industrial alcohol sold at a price of about 25 cents a gallon when made by the normal processes from Cuban molasses or synthetically from oil refinery gases. If made from grain in

* Successor to the O.P.M.
† Sale of stocks on hand was not affected by this proposal.

the whiskey distilleries, its cost was about a dollar per gallon. This high cost of the alcohol made from grain necessarily meant that any synthetic rubber produced from it would be two or three times as costly as synthetic rubber produced from petroleum or from cheap industrial alcohol. But this cost was only a money cost and not a reflection of the use of critical materials and skilled labor.

There remained only the question of whether it would require less time and less critical materials to convert the grain alcohol into butadiene than to produce butadiene from petroleum. Several engineering studies of these figures were made and it was concluded that it should be possible to erect new plants for the conversion of alcohol into butadiene more easily and quickly than to produce butadiene from butane. But the use of critical materials and the time required for building plants for the conversion of butylene to butadiene was about the same as for alcohol, and the types of critical materials used in the alcohol plants were somewhat different from the type used in the butylene plants. The alcohol and butylene processes were therefore good complements for each other.

In consequence of these studies, plans for the production of butadiene from butane were canceled or suspended and much of the oil program was shifted at once from butane to butylene as a raw material, using our new process. To make up for the capacity originally scheduled for production from butane, and which was not shifted to butylene, additional plants using alcohol as a raw material were authorized at this time by Rubber Reserve.

The effect on public opinion of these wholly constructive but seemingly belated changes in the program was most unfavorable. They confirmed the growing impression that those responsible for the production of synthetic rubber were not themselves sure of what they were doing.

By this time the whole petroleum industry had become

alarmed over the slow progress being made in synthetic rubber production. A technical committee of the Petroleum Industry War Council reviewed every possibility and concluded that by intensive cracking of kerosene and similar oil products, carried out in existing refinery units, with some changes, the oil industry could produce a considerable amount of butadiene within a period estimated to be about six months. As contrasted with the minimum estimate of twelve to eighteen months required for the construction of the main butadiene plants of the Rubber Reserve Company program, both the alcohol plants and the petroleum plants, this possibility seemed attractive.

The oil industry's technical committee obtained from us the designs and data on the plant of this type which we had put into operation in January, 1942. This plant had run continuously at full capacity. The butadiene from this operation was being currently converted into both Buna-N and Buna-S types of rubber by Standard itself at Baton Rouge. Some quantities were also being delivered to the rubber companies for their small operations.* Therefore, both the process and the product were commercially proven and it was only a matter of determining whether improvised plants of this kind based on existing refinery equipment would be practical.

The first estimates indicated that, within a period of six to twelve months, butadiene production as high as 150,000 tons per year might be attained through this "quickie" program of converting surplus equipment throughout the oil industry for the production of butadiene. It was clear that the cost of this butadiene would be very high because of the relative inefficiency of the makeshift plants and the lack of any facilities to

---

* The remaining supplies for the rubber companies were coming from small commercial plants operated by Dow, Carbide and Carbon Chemical and Shell Oil Companies, using processes not deemed suitable for large expansion.

recover and utilize products other than butadiene which were produced and which had made the Standard operation at Baton Rouge economical.

But, as in the case of the grain alcohol, this high cost was only a money cost which did not reflect use of critical materials or labor and seemed to be unimportant as compared with the consequences of a rubber famine.

The Rubber Reserve Company did not view this "quickie" scheme at all favorably and experience showed that their skepticism was justified. But the immediate result of this difference of opinion on the "quickie" program between the Rubber Reserve Company and the Petroleum Coordinator's office was further to confuse the rubber picture.

The mounting difficulties in the way of attaining butadiene production again threw into the limelight the possibilities of Butyl rubber as a means of getting some synthetic rubber production without waiting for butadiene production. On orders of Rubber Reserve Company, Standard was at the time enlarging its own pioneer Butyl plant, still under construction at Baton Rouge, Louisiana, to a capacity of 30,000 tons per annum. Although there had never been any commercial operation of such a plant, a second one of the same capacity had been authorized for Standard's affiliate, the Humble Oil and Refining Company at Baytown, Texas. This provided a total of 60,000 tons of Butyl rubber, production of which was scheduled to begin with the completion of Standard's first unit early in 1943. This rubber was not to be used in tires for which it was now universally agreed that it was not well suited, but only for tubes, (for which it seemed even better than natural rubber) and for miscellaneous goods.

We reviewed this situation and proposed possible plans for expanding the Butyl production to help meet the emergency. It was estimated that with some changes of design an additional expenditure of about 25 per cent might increase the capacity of the plants by more than 100 per cent.

These technical possibilities were discussed with Mr. Arthur Newhall who was then acting as Rubber Coordinator for the War Production Board and with the Rubber Reserve Company. As a result, Standard was directed to alter its designs so as to eliminate some of the original equipment ordered and supplement the remainder by additional equipment which it was hoped would give a total production of 132,000 tons of Butyl rubber, instead of 60,000 tons, without delaying the construction of the plants and without any net increase in critical material consumption. Unfortunately these hopes later proved to be too optimistic.

As a part of this effort to speed up Butyl development and make it more useful in the emergency, we also demonstrated the possibility of producing an inferior grade of Butyl rubber called Flexon. This was turned out in open wooden tubs in which cakes of dry ice were used as a refrigerant. The whole operation was reminiscent of bootleg liquor production in prohibition days and the Flexon was nicknamed "bath-tub rubber" by the press. Although the Flexon was not up to Butyl rubber in quality, tests by some of the rubber companies demonstrated that tires good enough for small passenger cars at moderate speeds could be made from this type of product. Certainly they would be far better than no tires at all. The oil industry's technical committee and the technical committee of the Rubber Reserve Company studied the Flexon operation and agreed that the possibilities of production of the product should be determined. This also proved to be an abortive development from a practical standpoint. No commercial production of Flexon was ever realized because of a combination of difficulties.

In those dark days the country was ready to listen to any plan which promised to keep automobiles on the road. The old schemes for wheels made of steel springs, or of wood with asphalt rims, designs for canvas tire covers and all possible substitutes for rubber tires were reviewed and many new varieties proposed. In Detroit, the technical as well as the production center of the automobile industry, a joint committee of automotive engineers and tire experts was set up under the chairmanship of Mr. J. G. Zeder of the Detroit section of the Society of Automotive Engineers. This committee considered first all known possibilities for using mechanical substitutes for rubber tires. It worked in close cooperation with Mr. Charles F. Kettering, technical head of General Motors and Mr. Fred M. Zeder, Vice Chairman of Chrysler, who had been asked to review all these substitutes for rubber tires by Mr. Jesse Jones. Mr. Kettering was chairman and Mr. Fred Zeder was a member of the National Inventors Council, and in that capacity they were part of Mr. Jones' official family, which at that time included the Patent Office.

It was soon concluded by these engineering experts that an automobile simply could not be kept on the road and in useful service by any known device save the rubber tire. The Detroit Committee then turned its attention to all possible expedients for prolonging wear of tires. It supervised test work on Flexon and also did a great deal of work on the use of Thiokol, the American synthetic rubber which had been produced on a small commercial scale since 1930. While it was well known that Thiokol could not be used directly for new tires, it was hoped that it might be practical for retreading worn tires. Some of the leading tire manufacturers were very active in this effort, but this road also eventually came to a dead end. The Thiokol was not satisfactory for general use and supplies of reclaimed rubber for re-treading purposes proved to be adequate.

It seems probable that all these efforts at improvised solutions of the rubber problem, however well intentioned and promising they may have seemed at the time, further accelerated the loss of public confidence during the spring and summer of 1942. The synthetic rubber program was becoming synonymous in the public mind with confusion and futility.

To make the collapse of confidence in the rubber program complete, only one further element was needed and that was supplied quite innocently by the British. Beginning early in 1942 Sir Clive Baillieu, head of the British Supply Mission in Washington, had begun to interest himself actively in the prospects for the production of synthetic rubber in the United States. He had delegated the task of following this to Mr. F. B. Clapp, an Australian industrialist who had been drafted to help the Mission. They had access to the government's data and were familiar with the views of all Washington official-dom. In addition, they were in direct contact with the companies engaged in the actual construction of plants for the program. They had only one question—was the United States really going to get any substantial production of Buna-S rubber in 1943? The British war plans depended on the answer to this question.

When Mr. Clapp came to see us we did our best to clarify the many misunderstandings. We pointed out that the widely circulated statements that no rubber had been or could be produced unless the butadiene were made from alcohol were entirely without foundation. Butadiene was butadiene no matter where it came from.

As for the date on which the full program on synthetic rubber would be running, we were not too sanguine. We were sure that Standard's Baton Rouge butadiene plants were going to be finished in the first half of 1943 and Humble's Baytown plants very soon afterward. The Carbide and Carbon Company's first plants, we were sure, would also be running in the first half of the year. The first styrene plants would certainly be running and Buna-S polymerizing plants of adequate capacity for all this butadiene and styrene presented no special difficulties.

But, as to the completion of the entire butadiene and styrene program, there was much uncertainty. Time had certainly been lost and the delivery dates of a large amount of critical construction material for all of the later plants in the program were wholly unpredictable. If the Army and Navy continued to demand these critical materials for other uses the rubber program might be delayed indefinitely. In addition to these physical factors, the prolonged controversy had created an atmosphere which was paralyzing initiative. Every action on synthetic rubber by Government or by industry had now to be judged by the criticism which would probably be made of it. The Rubber Reserve Company and industry were fighting against this paralyzing influence but the effect could not be denied. All we could tell the British was that we were sure the early part of the program which had been started ahead of the worst jam on critical construction materials would be completed and running successfully by the middle of 1943. The remainder of the program was beyond prediction.

After the first meetings with us, Mr. Clapp returned to say that the British experts in London seemed to be very pessimistic about even the first part of the program. London had decided that it was necessary to send special representatives of their Ministry to the United States to make an independent study of the rubber situation.

This seemed to complete the picture. The public and the press had long ago lost confidence; the Congress had lost confidence; and now apparently our allies, the British, to whom the best official and unofficial information was available, had also lost confidence. This was known to many people in Washington, and to some, at least, it seemed the last straw.

In early June the special representatives of the British Ministry of Supply nominated by the Synthetic Rubber Committee of that Ministry arrived in the United States to begin their independent survey of the status of the American rubber program.

It appeared almost immediately that the main reason for the

concern of the technical experts in England over the future
of the American synthetic rubber program was their impression that the bulk of the American program depended upon
the conversion of butane into butadiene. While this process
was sound in principle, the British technical experts were convinced (correctly, as the event proved) that the operating
difficulties which would be met with in the first large plants
based on this process would cause long delays. Their gravest
doubts were removed when they found that this butane
process which they distrusted had been almost eliminated
from the program and that the great bulk of the butadiene
would be produced from butylene and from alcohol by the
two new processes of Standard and Carbide and Carbon.

Within a short time the British representatives had satisfied
themselves completely as to the technical soundness of the
American butadiene program and of the Buna rubber production which depended upon it. If the program did not succeed it could only be because of failure of the governmental
coordination. They returned to London in late August, taking with them a reassuring report.

But in the meantime, the American situation had reached
bottom. On July 21 the House of Representatives Committee
on Agriculture reported favorably, without amendment, a
resolution embodying the bill which had been worked out by
Senator Gillette's sub-committee and already passed by the
Senate. The House passed it at once. Thus there came to the
President, with a decisive vote of the Congress, the "Rubber
Supply Act of 1942."

This act would have established a new and entirely independent agency with unlimited powers "to make available at
the earliest possible time an adequate supply of rubber." That
rubber was to come from alcohol, but "alcohol" was defined
by the act as any chemical derivative from any agricultural or
forest product. Neither the War Production Board, the Army
or Navy, nor any executive agency of Government was to

have any right to interfere with this new rubber agency. The Congress had made up its mind that the country could not live, and certainly not fight a war, without rubber for the nation's motor transport. There was no longer any confidence in the success of the program being worked out by the executive branch of the government with the aid of the oil, chemical, and rubber industries. Congress was going to produce from the farms by its own independent agent the tire rubber which the country absolutely had to have.

On August 6 the President vetoed this desperate plan in a 2500-word message—one of the strongest ever written. He pointed out that this new rubber agency of Congress would create chaos in the whole Allied war program.

CHAPTER XVIII

THE BARUCH COMMITTEE

Whatever might be the weight of the President's objections to Congress' "Rubber Supply Act of 1942," mere negative action would not suffice. Without rubber road transportation would break down and without road transportation the complex production mechanism of America would begin to disintegrate and the war would be lost before it really began. There was no longer any confidence in the national synthetic rubber program. What was to be done?

The end of the President's veto message of August 6, 1942, provided the answer:

(Veto Message)

In recent months there have been so many conflicting statements of fact concerning all the elements of the rubber situation—statements from responsible Government agencies as well as from private sources that I have set up a committee of three men to investigate the whole situation—to get the facts—and to report them to me as quickly as possible with their recommendations.

This committee will immediately proceed to study the present supply, the estimated military and essential civilian needs, and the various processes now being urged; and they will recommend processes to be used, not only in the light of need for rubber, but also in the light of critical materials required by these processes. In a sense this will require a review of the program now being followed by the War Production Board. It will form a basis for future action not only with respect to synthetic rubber, but also such matters as Nation-wide gas rationing and motor transportation. The responsibility for the distribution of critical materials will continue to remain with the War Production Board; but the

Board, as well as the American people, will have a complete statement before them of the facts found by the committee.

This unusual investigation is being directed because of the interest of the American people in the subject, because of the great impact of the lack of rubber upon the lives of American citizens, and because of the present confusion of thought and factual statement.

In the meantime, of course, the manufacture of synthetic rubber from oil and grain will continue without interruption.

The functions of this committee require not only experience in business and production and the relations of government thereto, but also trained, scientific minds. Therefore, I am appointing as members of this committee, Hon. Bernard M. Baruch, chairman; Dr. James D. Conant, president of Harvard University; and Dr. Karl T. Compton, president of Massachusetts Institute of Technology. They will be equipped with adequate staff, and will, I know, submit their report at the earliest possible moment. I am asking them to investigate the whole situation and to recommend such action as will produce the rubber necessary for our total war effort, including essential civilian use, with a minimum interference with the production of other weapons of war.

FRANKLIN D. ROOSEVELT.

The White House
August 6, 1942.

The appointment of the Baruch Rubber Committee was probably the most widely acclaimed action on the domestic front in the history of the war program. The public, the press, the Congress, Washington officialdom, and the rubber, oil and chemical industries engaged in the rubber program breathed a sigh of relief which swelled to a gale of approval.

To those of us who were actively engaged in carrying out the program, it was apparent immediately that this confidence was not misplaced. Almost before the ink on the announcements was dry, the Committee had organized itself and started its job.

In the general division of duties in the synthetic rubber study, Dr. Compton assumed supervision of the investigation of the rubber polymerization processes and related problems, and Dr. Conant, the supervision of the butadiene studies. The procedure of the Committee in its contact with Standard was typical. Dr. Conant telephoned to explain that he had selected a sub-committee under the chairmanship of Mr. E. P. Stevenson, a leading independent chemical engineer, to make the field studies on the butadiene problem. He asked us to arrange at once to receive this sub-committee and to assist them in their work.

The sub-committee began its work by meetings in New York with the members of our technical executive staff. It then proceeded to the central Esso Laboratories of Standard Oil Development Company at Bayway, N.J., for sessions of several days and from there to the Baton Rouge Refinery where butadiene and Buna rubber were already being manufactured and where the new plants, which were to form the design basis for the government's principal program, were under construction. The members of the sub-committee interviewed the research leaders and engineers who were engaged in the rubber program, examined the pertinent laboratory data and pilot plants and took away with them copies of the important reports and engineering information.

In the meantime, Dr. Conant himself followed other important angles of the matter directly with us, giving his personal attention especially to the much disputed question of whether the oil industry could find sufficient butylene to carry through its main program of butadiene production. In this study he brought together in Washington the engineers and refinery executives most concerned and the experts from the Petroleum Coordinator's office.

The spirit and manner of conducting the study by the Baruch Committee disarmed criticism and stilled controversy. The government officials and private interests concerned in the rubber program were quite certain in advance of completion of the Baruch report that it would clear away the mountain of doubt and confusion which had been built up during the preceding months and give at last a clear picture of the national synthetic rubber development.

This predisposition on the part of the public and all of the interested experts to believe that the report would put an end to the rubber controversy was confirmed when the report was issued on September 10, 1942. The text of the general findings of the report and of the detailed discussion dealing with the synthetic rubber problem read:

REPORT OF THE SPECIAL COMMITTEE TO STUDY THE
RUBBER SITUATION

1. *Statement of the Problem*

Of all critical and strategic materials, rubber is the one which presents the greatest threat to the safety of our nation and the success of the Allied cause. Production of steel, copper, aluminum, alloys or aviation gasoline may be inadequate to prosecute the war as rapidly and effectively as we could wish, but at the worst we still are assured of sufficient supplies of these items to operate our armed forces on a very powerful scale. But if we fail to secure quickly a large new rubber supply our war effort and our domestic economy both will collapse. Thus the rubber situation gives rise to our most critical problem.

Our position with respect to this vital commodity may be briefly outlined as follows:

The demands now placed upon us are enormous. Without any allowance whatsoever for civilian passenger car tires, the estimated requirements for the year 1943 are 574,000 tons. This contrasts with the total average over-all consumption in the United States before the war of over 600,000 tons. We must supply not only the needs of our own armed forces but much of those of the military machines of our Allies as well. We must equip our buses and trucks and other commercial vehicles and provide on a large scale specialty items for such purposes as factory belting, surgical, hospital and health supplies. And in addition to all these we *must* maintain the tires on at least a substantial portion of our 27,000,-000 civilian passenger automobiles. Otherwise an economy geared to rubber-borne motor transport to an extent not approached elsewhere in the world will break down.

To meet these demands we may look to four main sources of supply:

First. Our present stockpile of natural rubber and such additions as may come to it from natural rubber imports from Latin America, Africa, and other rubber-producing lands. These are comparatively small.

Second. Our present stockpile of scrap rubber, estimated as sufficiently large with yearly additions to operate our reclaiming industry at present capacity through the year 1945.

Third. The production of synthetic rubbers.

Fourth. We possess in the tires of our automobiles a priceless reserve, which must be guarded with greatest care. It represents a stockpile of some 1,000,000 tons of rubber applicable to the uses of our civilian transportation and the needs of the day to day life of our people.

Having lost to Japan 90 per cent of our prewar source of natural rubber, chief reliance on new supplies of rubber must be placed on the new synthetic rubber program. But to obtain this in time we must, within two years after Pearl Harbor, have created one of the largest industries in the country. Normally such a development would require a dozen years. To compress it into less than two years is an almost superhuman task.

Our Committee is convinced that the Government's present program is technically sound. From this time on the important thing is to get on with it without further delay.

In drawing up the recommendations which follow the Committee has sought to find a basis upon which the entire nation can go forward together, uniting our energies against the enemy instead of dissipating them in domestic wrangling. It appreciates that it is asking the public to make sacrifices because of mistakes that have been made and for which the people are not to blame. But wrong things done in the past cannot be cited as a defense for making mistakes in the future. The war demands that we go forward from this point united and resolved to win at any cost.

2. Procedure of the Committee

This Committee was asked "to get the facts and make recommendations." To this end, immediately after its appointment it assembled a competent technical staff of approximately twenty-five men of whose competence we had knowledge through first-hand experience. With the aid of this group the Committee has endeavored as far as humanly possible in the time at our disposal to get the facts and draw from these facts the logical conclusions.

With the aid of experts in the art of rubber manufacture and rubber compounding and with the assistance of a group of chemists and chemical engineers, we checked so far as possible the chemical processes involved in the government program and those suggested by individuals and companies not yet included in this program. For this purpose members of our staff traveled throughout the eastern, southern, and middle western sections of the country, examining plants, consulting the technical experts concerned with the progress of the program and in the construction of new facilities. With their aid, we also examined carefully the present status of all tests throwing light on the adequacy of the new synthetic materials for military and civilian purposes, as well as the potentialities of numerous materials which have been suggested for the recapping of tires or special uses in the rubber program. We also examined at first hand into the condition and state of protection of the nation's stockpile, which must serve as the essential backlog of our efforts until synthetic materials can be brought into substantial production.

Special checks likewise were made by men competent in business and engineering associated with the Committee, as to the rate of construction of scheduled plants and the situation with respect to the allocation of strategic materials to these plants and the granting of the necessary priorities. The capacity of the country to produce the essential raw materials for the development of the synthetic program also was checked. We have endeavored with the aid of competent assistance to evaluate the potential requirements of this country and the United Nations and have made our estimates of the probable supply, present or to come.

In addition to interviewing, through our staff, a number of persons familiar with the various aspects of the rubber situation, we heard formally many officials of the Government as well as representatives of industry. A great number of documents from governmental and other sources were put at our disposal, and we examined these records with care. The printed records of hearings before the committees of Congress which deal with this subject run to many pages. We reviewed the evidence thus presented as of value on many points. All of the Congressional Committees who had interested themselves in the problem were asked for their suggestions or recommendations and many stimulating suggestions were made. Particularly helpful were the Committees under the chairmanships of Senators Truman, Gillette and Murray. In conclusion, it is a pleasure to acknowledge that from all with whom we have been in touch we have received the maximum of cooperation.

· · · · · ·

6. The Synthetic Program

The present plans for the production of synthetic rubber as outlined to us by the governmental agencies concerned call for the erection of the following types of plants in the United States: *

The Committee has examined the present status of the Government's schedules and estimates that if the construction program can be met on the dates specified there will be produced during 1943: 400,000 tons of Buna-S; 30,000 tons of neoprene (in part from private sources). We believe that these processes will ultimately work on a large scale and yield satisfactory products.

Furthermore, our experts estimate that the time required to get the various plants running smoothly under actual operating conditions will not be so lengthy as to cause serious delay. On the other hand it must be remembered that we are dealing here with a new industry and that in the production of Buna-S three separate manufacturing operations are concerned, no one of which has been carried out as yet on anything approaching the present contemplated scale.

Therefore, until more experience has been gained by the operation of one of the large-scale units at each step, we must consider that a considerable element of risk is present in the picture. The importance of completing rapidly one full-scale plant using each process and the erection of pilot plants is considered in the technical section of this report.

The Committee wishes to emphasize once again at this point that the whole question of obtaining synthetic rubbers in adequate amounts in 1943 hinges on the rate of construction of the manufacturing plants. Unless the present situation involving the assigning of priorities and allocating of materials is improved, there is grave danger that there will be serious delays in the completion of the plants and consequent reduction in the amount of

* Tabular list given on p. 187.

synthetic materials produced. Furthermore, unless the administrative changes recommended in a later section of this report are put into effect, conflicting governmental plans with respect to the oil industry may seriously jeopardize the production of butadiene.

We have also examined with the aid of our experts many other processes for the production of butadiene and synthetic rubber. We find that quite apart from their merits or demerits, no one of them could be substituted in the present program with hope of accelerating the production of Buna-S in the critical year 1943.

We would be blind if we did not see the efforts now in progress on the part of many companies to have a part in the development of a large new industry with vast postwar possibilities. This has been accentuated in the minds of the petroleum producers by gasoline rationing with its attendant loss of sales. They are thus forced to turn to other products including butadiene. Furthermore, we are not unaware that it is inevitable that once the war is over there will be a struggle amongst various groups for the control of this new industry. But all such considerations cannot affect this Committee as to its conclusions. We are concerned only with the production of the largest amount of rubber in the minimum amount of time in order to carry the country successfully through the war. It is our firm conclusion that present processes for manufacturing synthetic rubber and the raw materials required (butadiene and styrene) must not at this late date be changed unless new processes can be shown beyond peradventure to have such advantages over those now employed that more rubber would be obtained in the ensuing months than would otherwise be the case. We have found no such process in the course of our investigations.

The Committee finds that there has been considerable discussion between two groups within the oil industry as to whether or not there was a serious conflict between the butadiene program based on butylene and the high octane aviation gasoline program. With the aid of our experts we have examined carefully into this problem and consulted many technologists in various oil companies as well as discussing the matter with the officials of the Office of Petroleum Coordinator. It is our conclusion that, while the possibility of a conflict between the two programs does exist, it need not become serious if the possibility is recognized and if the administration of these two closely related enterprises is properly integrated.

The necessity for the administrative changes along these lines which are recommended elsewhere in this report is further demonstrated by the uncertainty of the stated aviation requirements both in quantity and quality. The evidence clearly indicates that if the present demands for high octane aviation gasoline and butadiene stay where they now are, there need be no conflict.

If and when the armed services should decide that such larger quantities of high octane aviation gasoline are needed, there are ways by which this demand can be met by the industry without diminishing the flow of butylene to the butadiene plants.

It is fortunate that the program for the needed plants is generally in the hands of as competent engineers as there are in the country. Probably the most interesting and satisfying part of our study is the confidence we have acquired in the men from industry who have the plans in hand and who are satisfied they can lick the problem in the given time. Their competence and experience, their resourcefulness and ingenuity are the best guarantees we have that they can do so. We have been much impressed with the fact that this stupendous undertaking is only possible because of the highly developed skill of our technologists. No one could have examined the facts before us without appreciating the magnitude and scope of the task; no one could have made this study without realizing that because of the shortsightedness and failure to act on technically sound advice we must now proceed with insufficient experience. On this basis we venture the statement that never on the basis of so little has so much been involved. Under these uncertainties the only recourse is to provide ample margins when in doubt.

. . . .

The report itself was accepted with the same unanimous acclaim which the appointment of the Committee had met. It brought up to an even higher level the public's confidence in and affection for Bernard Baruch. Although his services to his country on other matters through two wars were certainly more arduous and perhaps more important than this short episode in his life, the successful completion of this task will probably always be best remembered as typical of his genius. The character of the man and his methods of dealing with industry, methods which he had employed so successfully as commander of industrial mobilization in the United States during the first World War are well illustrated by the following incident.

Shortly after the issuance of the report, Mr. Farish told me that Mr. Baruch would like to see us about synthetic rubber. We had had no contact with him at all on the subject of the inquiry and were entirely at sea as to what to expect. We were not left in doubt for a moment. Mr. Baruch had two things on his mind. The first was to tell us, in no uncertain terms, that the rubber program was not the government's job but industry's job, and that the government and all of its officials only functioned to serve industry in getting the job done. Therefore, our duty was not to stand on ceremony or to be backward but to consider that it was up to us to "raise hell" with everybody in Washington who wasn't moving fast enough in helping us on any part of the rubber job that we had to do. Then he asked us rather challengingly whether we had yet been busy along that line. We were relieved to be able to tell him that we had. Even before Mr. Jeffers, the new Rubber Director, had had a chance to get his bearings, we had urgently requested his earliest help in trying to get deliveries of long delayed equipment for the construction of our butadiene plants. The equipment manufacturers were protesting that they had higher priority orders from Washington for other purposes. Something had to be done at once. Mr. Jeffers had promised me that these priority disputes would be his first order of business as soon as he could get his office organized. So we hoped that we had emerged from this first Baruch test successfully.

But Mr. Baruch's next point was not so easy. He said the bottleneck of the whole program would certainly be the butadiene. He was clear in his own mind that the critical factors in the butadiene program were simply the ability of the Standard and of the Carbide and Carbon companies to make their new butadiene processes work immediately and successfully and to get their own plants finished and running on schedule. These were the foundations on which everything else would have to rest. Then he turned to us and said "I know you can do it, and if you don't, I'll take your hides off."

After that meeting it was not until May, 1943, when our most important butadiene plant was running successfully, that I felt sure my hide was going to stay with me.

CHAPTER XIX

THE RUBBER DIRECTOR

Pursuant to the recommendations of the Baruch Committee the President, on September 17, 1942, issued an Executive Order creating the Office of Rubber Director, with broad powers cutting across the jurisdiction of all other government agencies and concentrating in one man responsibility for "technical research and development, importation, purchase, sale, acquisition, storage, transportation, provision of facilities, conservation, production, manufacturing, processing, marketing, distribution, and use of natural and synthetic rubber, related materials, and products manufactured therefrom." William M. Jeffers, of Omaha, Nebraska, President of the Union Pacific Railroad, was appointed Rubber Director.

Mr. Jeffers brought to this task an aura of forceful effectiveness, which at once captured the imagination of the public. He represented the antithesis of the scandal mongering, confusion, and futility which had been the net impression of the rubber program left in the public mind by the prolonged controversy of 1942. He was a representative American of the kind the nation turns to instinctively for action when real trouble is at the door.

Certainly, trouble was at our door when the capable hands of the new Rubber Director took the reins in September, 1942. The Baruch Committee was not exaggerating in the statement:

"If we fail to secure quickly a large new rubber supply, our war effort and our domestic economy will both collapse."

The only possible solution was

"by 'bulling through' the present gigantic synthetic program
and by safeguarding jealously every ounce of rubber in the
country."

These were Mr. Jeffers' sailing orders. He framed them
and hung them above his desk. His conception of his job was
so simple and direct that no amount of bureaucratic compli-
cation or opposition had any effect on him. His position was
that he had been instructed by the President to carry out the
recommendations of the Baruch Report, and that they were
going to be carried out. Any individual or any other war
problem which seemed to interfere must get out of the way;
it could not stand on the track of the rubber program.

The organization which Mr. Jeffers set up was headed by
Colonel Bradley Dewey, whom he selected as his Deputy.
This was the same Colonel Dewey whose appointment to
supervise the whole effort had been suggested by Mr. Deupree at the joint meeting of the O.P.M., Rubber Reserve and
industry technologists of May 21, 1941, when the Rubber
Reserve Company's 40,000-ton program had been launched.
Mr. Jeffers described his organization in these terms: "My
job is to run interference for Colonel Dewey." This was in
fact the way the work of the rubber program was carried
through. Someone had to lead and knock out or brush aside
all opposition. Behind this leader there had to be a highly
organized technical staff for reaching all of the detailed decisions and carrying through the administration of the program.

The staff of the Rubber Director's office was at the outset
recruited in part from the Rubber Reserve Company, in part
from the War Production Board, and in part from industry
and universities. Mr. M. J. Madigan, a special assistant to the
Under Secretary of War who had been acting as Chief Engi-

neer for the Rubber Reserve Company, became the acting Chief Engineer for the Rubber Director's office, but soon returned to the War Department and was replaced by Mr. Frank R. Creedon, who had been in charge of the construction program for the explosive plants of the War Department which were just then being completed. The principal administrators of the organization, in addition to the Chief Engineer, were executives of three of the leading rubber companies who were drafted for this service. Mr. L. D. Tompkins of the United States Rubber Company became head of the division of operations and allocations; Mr. E. B. Babcock of Firestone Tire and Rubber Company became head of the testing, compounding and utilization section; and Dr. R. P. Dinsmore of the Goodyear Company was made head of the research and development section. Dr. E. R. Gilliland of Massachusetts Institute of Technology became the chief technical advisor and later Deputy Director.

Close working relations were established between the Rubber Director's office, the Rubber Reserve Company and the Petroleum Coordinator's office. The plan of the organization was that the Rubber Reserve Company would remain the permanent agency of the government responsible for the production of synthetic rubber and the Petroleum Coordinator's office the permanent agency responsible for the coordination of the oil industry in its rubber responsibilities, whereas the function of the Rubber Director's office was to carry out the recommendations of the Baruch Committee for the rapid and successful upbuilding of the new synthetic rubber industry. In the field of these other agencies, the Rubber Director's office therefore undertook to do only those things which were part of its emergency task. This left the program in condition for its permanent administration by the other governmental agencies. This sound plan resulted in the establishment of harmonious relations between the large and aggressive emergency organization of the Rubber Director, functioning officially as a part of the War Production Board, and the organizations administered by Mr. Jones and Mr. Ickes.

In the carrying out of the Baruch Report recommendations on synthetic rubber, the Jeffers regime had two major problems. The first, and by all means the more important, was simply to "bull through" the existing program of the Rubber Reserve Company. In its essence, this gigantic program was found to be wholly sound, a monument to the business judgment of Mr. Jones and the ability of the compact little working organization of the Rubber Reserve Company which had been carrying this burden since the outbreak of the war, for a large part of the time handicapped by criticism and accusation.

"Bulling through" the Rubber Reserve Company's program consisted first of all in speeding up the actual construction of the plants already under way and in solving the problems which were delaying the starting of construction on plants which had been authorized but not yet begun. In addition to these primary duties, the Jeffers regime had to work out the supplementary recommendations of the report providing for additional production of butadiene both from oil and from alcohol, additional research, development and pilot plant work, increases in the production of neoprene and Thiokol specialty rubbers, and, most difficult of all to plan and execute, the actual conversion of the rubber industry from natural to synthetic rubber.

As the Rubber Reserve Company had anticipated, the crystallization of plans for so-called "quickie" butadiene plants turned out to be much more difficult than had first appeared. Whereas the Baruch Committee had recommended the addition of 100,000 tons of butadiene capacity from this program, it was found practical to authorize at once only a portion of this. Most of it was later canceled due to the coincidence of two factors. The first was the delay which had intervened in actually working out the plans for these projects. Before this difficulty had been cleared away, new data on the probable capacity of the plants of the regular butadiene program provided the necessary assurance that most of these supplementary plants would not be needed.

Only five plants in the "quickie" program actually served in any very important way the original purpose of providing a quick supply of butadiene to bridge over the period between the completion of the rubber polymerization units and the completion of the butadiene plants making up the regular program. Two of these plants were put together quickly by Standard and its affiliate Humble, mostly from old equipment. Two more were built in neighboring refineries and produced crude butadiene which was sent to the first two plants for purification. One very valuable makeshift plant was improvised in California by combining some facilities in the gas works of the Southern California Gas Company with others in a nearby oil refinery of the Shell Oil Company.

As the program developed, it also seemed possible to eliminate completely the production of Thiokol and to reduce the production of both neoprene and Butyl rubber. These specialty rubbers had been looked upon by the Baruch Committee as means of supplementing the supply of Buna-S rubber and providing further insurance against any delays or difficulties which might be experienced in the production or utilization of the Buna-S rubber. As the Buna-S program proceeded, the elements of doubt involved became less and less, and the necessity of exercising the utmost economy in the use of critical materials in the rubber program, in order to release these materials for the construction of escort vessels, planes, 100-octane plants, and other vital war programs, justified the lopping off of these supplementary recommendations of the Baruch Committee.

One other recommendation of the Baruch Committee had dealt with Russia. The Committee urged that an immediate effort be made to obtain the experience of the Russians in the production of synthetic rubber and make use of it in the American program.

The Rubber Director had attacked this problem but results were slow and disappointing. The Russians were producing on a large scale only the original Buna type synthetic rubber, butadiene polymerized by sodium. They seemed to have no experience with the improved Buna-S type or with the emulsion polymerization method on which the German and American programs were based. But for whatever use it might be, the Rubber Director's office persevered in the effort to get the Russian experience. The negotiations to exchange technical information and right of access to the manufacturing plants dragged. A special rubber mission, headed by Mr. Ernest W. Pittman, President of Inter-Chemical Company, was sent to Russia but, in the absence of a detailed agreement, the mission was able to visit only one plant and even here failed to get the technical data most wanted.

In the course of the negotiations, the Russians asked for information on the American processes of making synthetic ethyl alcohol from petroleum gases. While the United States was converting surplus grain to alcohol for butadiene production, the Russians needed all their grain for food and wished to use petroleum gases to make additional alcohol to increase their butadiene production. Standard was asked by the Rubber Director to discuss this matter with the Russians, and with the assistance of the State Department, a detailed agreement was negotiated.* The agreement provided for inspection by the Russians of Standard's Baton Rouge alcohol plant and for the furnishing of designs, specifications and operating instructions. Pursuant to this agreement, the first Russian inspection party, headed by Mr. P. S. Makeev, Vice Peoples' Commissar and Chief, Rubber Mission of U.S.S.R., arrived in Baton

*A similar agreement was made between du Pont and the Russians concerning the neoprene process on which the Russians had asked for detailed information.

Rouge on October 27, 1943. Colonel Dewey, who had now succeeded Mr. Jeffers as Rubber Director, had proposed that, while in Baton Rouge, the Russian Mission be given an opportunity to see something of the rubber plants there. This courtesy was intended by the Rubber Director to be in the nature of a return for the limited privileges extended to the American Mission and to aid his negotiations on more complete exchange of reports on synthetic rubber. It required an authorization from U.S. Army Intelligence which he was to obtain and which Mr. Makeev, before leaving Washington, understood would be awaiting his arrival at Baton Rouge. Due to some new general regulations by the Army on "courtesy visits" to war plants by allied missions, the Rubber Director was unable, however, to obtain clearance from the Army for the visit to any plants other than the alcohol plant, which was covered by the detailed agreement. The result was that Mr. Makeev and the members of his mission were already in Baton Rouge expecting to see the rubber plants and Standard's local management was not authorized to permit the visit.

When I learned of the situation, there was no time to inquire how it could have arisen. It seemed clear, however, that the result would be that the good faith or good will of the Americans in their dealings with the Russians on rubber would be questioned. I reported the facts by telephone to Mr. Stettinius, who was then Under Secretary of State, and whose most difficult duties at this very moment were concerned with Russian contacts. Within two hours a message from the Military Intelligence Section of the General Staff in Washington advised us that the Army had issued the necessary instructions to permit this courtesy visit by the Russian Rubber Mission to the Baton Rouge rubber plants. The Mission made the visit as planned and expressed itself as well pleased with the manner in which the understanding with the Rubber Director had been carried out.

This incident suggested that perhaps a part of the difficulty which the American Rubber Mission had experienced in Russia might have been the result of tangles within the Russian bureaucracy rather than any considered decision to withhold data. But whatever may have been the cause, the hopes of the Baruch Committee for some effective help from Russia on the American synthetic rubber program were never fulfilled.

Under the Jeffers regime, there were instituted more complete and broader arrangements for the exchange of technical information and for the stimulation of research and development work in synthetic rubber. The technical organizations of some large industrial units which had no direct connection with the production of synthetic rubber, but were interested in its utilization for special purposes, were drawn in. Dr. R. R. Williams of the Bell Telephone Laboratories became chairman of a research group. Aggressive programs of research in university laboratories were begun with the help of government funds. As an aid to the program, the four largest rubber companies, who had been signatories to the December 19, 1941, cooperative agreement with Standard and the Rubber Reserve Company waived the secrecy clauses in this agreement, permitting the Rubber Director's office to proceed with an entirely free hand in working out its arrangements for Committee work and for the widest exchange of technical information which could serve the purpose of the program.

The actual construction program was now moving fast. The American public was by this time convinced that the nation was on the point of building up a new basic industry of synthetic rubber production; there was time now to think of the future of this industry. If it followed the normal course for new industries built with private capital it would have to pass through a period of strong competitive effort not only in the field of scientific development and of commercial rivalry but also in the courts as the result of litigation on conflicting patents. To protect the government's investment the

Rubber Reserve Company had solved this problem for itself by the agreement of December, 1941. This agreement also substituted cooperation for litigation among the five companies who were then the only ones working on Buna type synthetic rubber. Later several additional groups of the smaller rubber companies had been brought into the program as producers of Buna rubber in government-owned plants. Several hundred rubber companies, manufacturing special rubber products, and many chemical companies and other industrial units were also now active in the field of synthetic rubber. Although there was a general willingness to subordinate private interests to success of the government's own program, it was the conclusion of the Rubber Director's office that the government program itself would be greatly stimulated and a much broader foundation for a postwar synthetic rubber industry which would deserve and receive public support, would be built if some means could be found to reduce or eliminate patent litigation in the main lines of the synthetic rubber industry.

At the request of the Rubber Director's office, this problem was studied by all of the companies most interested. The first definite proposal for a solution of the problem is reported in my letter to Colonel Dewey of January 27, 1943, as follows:

I regret very much that you were unable to be with us today at the discussion Mr. Gallagher * and myself had with Mr. Collyer and Mr. Jett of the Goodrich Company.

The conclusion reached at this discussion was that the four of us would like to meet with you at the earliest possible date to explore the possibility of some arrangement under which the royalty or compensation to be paid to patent owners for licenses under their synthetic rubber patents would be left open for the

* Mr. Gallagher was then President of Standard Oil Company (N.J.) having succeeded Mr. Farish who died on November 29, 1942. Mr. Collyer and Mr. Jett were President and Secretary respectively of the B. F. Goodrich Company.

present and settled by arbitration either in the near future or after the war.

This is the same proposal which we made to the Rubber Reserve Company during our original discussions with them on the licensing by us of the Government's rubber program, and the same proposal which we renewed at the time of the negotiation of the December 19, 1941 agreement.

Until the meeting, Mr. Collyer had not been informed of these earlier proposals by us for arbitration, nor had we been informed that he also had urged arbitration of this entire question.

We all desired to proceed as rapidly as possible on this matter, but it appeared that the earliest date at which all four of us could be in Washington would be next Monday morning, and I therefore today telegraphed you as per the enclosed.

This proposal for a general pool of synthetic rubber patents, with licenses to everyone and royalties fixed and divided by arbitration was discussed by the officers of Standard and Goodrich with the Rubber Director's office a few days later and quickly reduced to the form of a memorandum by the Goodrich officers. The Rubber Director's office canvassed the sentiment of industry on this Goodrich-Standard proposal and reported that, while no one interposed any objections in theory, the practical objections to arbitrating these complicated questions were so deep-rooted and so generally expressed, that it was hopeless to proceed with this plan. Thus for the third time in the history of the government synthetic rubber development, arbitration as a means of avoiding controversy over patents, and securing immediate cooperation, was rejected on the ground of impracticability.

The Rubber Director's office continued to study the problem and on March 17, 1943, Colonel Dewey wrote me as follows:

This is to ask if you will advise upon what terms your company will sell to the Government all its synthetic rubber patent rights which are the subject of the agreement with Rubber Reserve Company and others dated December 19, 1941.

What I have in mind is an assignment of the entire right, title and interest of your company in such patents and patent rights, including benefits under outstanding licenses, with your company continuing as a party to the agreement, holding a non-exclusive royalty-free license.

The plan which underlaid this idea of a purchase by the government of Standard Oil's synthetic rubber patent rights included in the agreement of December 19, 1941, was a very ingenious one and at first looked as though it might be practical. The thought was that if the government itself acquired full and clear title to all the basic patents on Buna rubber, it could then turn to all individuals and companies interested in the potentialities of synthetic rubber and offer to grant them a free license under the basic patents but only on the condition that they were to give a free license to the government and to everyone else under their own improvement patents. On March 22, 1943, I replied to this letter as follows:

I have reviewed with my associates your letter of March 18 requesting us to advise upon what terms we will sell to the Government our patent rights and royalty interests in the Buna and related types of synthetic rubber covered by our contract of December 19, 1941 with Rubber Reserve Company and several rubber companies.

We all know from our many discussions that you have given this whole problem the most careful consideration and, while the solution you now propose is quite different from any we have heretofore had in mind, we realize the need for action and we accept your judgment of what is now required in the national interest. In accordance with your request we are ready to proceed at once as follows:

1. All of our interests in the patents and royalties to be immediately sold and delivered by us to the appropriate Government agency, subject of course to our present obligations.

2. The purchase price to be the fair value of the rights and interests sold, this fair value to be established by an impartial appraisal under a definite appraisal procedure established in the contract of sale.

We appreciate your expression of satisfaction with the cooperation you have received from us in the past and while we have not yet had an opportunity to review your proposal with legal counsel we would anticipate no special difficulty in concluding with the representatives of the Government at an early date a mutually satisfactory contract of sale along the above lines.

Within a short time after this letter of March 22, Colonel Dewey arranged for a discussion of the problem in Washington. In the meantime, objections arose which seemed to be serious both from the standpoint of the government and from our own standpoint. Serious doubts were expressed by counsel for the Rubber Reserve Company on the legality of a purchase of patents by the government and the subsequent attempted use of these patents as legal weapons to bargain with others. The legal theory here was that in the absence of express constitutional or even statutory authority the federal government cannot acquire a valid business monopoly running against the private rights of its citizens by the device of granting a patent and then buying the patent. From our own standpoint also there were many practical objections which we had reluctantly decided to waive when the government asked us to sell.

Real difficulties from the standpoint of Standard were also presented by the desire of the Rubber Reserve Company, if it went ahead on the plan, to proceed upon the basis of direct negotiation of a price rather than permitting the price to be fixed by impartial appraisers. This direct negotiation would have put upon Standard itself the responsibility for the price fixed, which was a most unwelcome and difficult position. If Standard were to agree to a low price, it would tend to belittle the value of Standard's interest in the patents and of the effort and struggle which it had put into this synthetic rubber development. On the other hand, if the negotiated price were commensurate with the real value and importance to the nation of the basic Buna patents, it might seem so high that Standard would appear to be a profiteer. Still another important difficulty was presented by the unsolved legal question of just what rights in the Buna rubber patents had passed into the hands of the Alien Property Custodian by his "vesting" of all I.G. property rights on the outbreak of the war.

The solution which was finally evolved out of the consideration of all these problems is summarized in the following exchange of correspondence between Mr. Gallagher and Mr. Jeffers.

April 15, 1943

Dear Mr. Jeffers:

In order to give the greatest possible impetus to the wartime rubber program and to encourage synthetic rubber development, we propose to transfer to the Government (through Rubber Reserve Company) Buna patent rights which form the basis of the national synthetic rubber program, under a plan which may be summarized as follows:

1. Rubber Reserve Company would have a free license for itself, not only for the war but for the life of the patents. (Neither the Government nor private interests now pay any royalties during the war.)

2. Rubber Reserve Company would also have the right to issue perpetual free licenses to everyone who cooperates with the Government in its war rubber program, and who reciprocates with similar licenses under its own patents.

3. Under this offer, there would be no payment to us or to others for the patent rights used, but the Government would agree to continue and expand its expenditures for research in the synthetic rubber field up to an aggregate amount of not less than $5,000,000.

If you agree with us that this proposal is in the public interest, we should like to submit and recommend it to our stockholders at our forthcoming annual meeting.

Very truly yours,
R. W. Gallagher

. . . .

April 17, 1943

Dear Mr. Gallagher:

Receipt is acknowledged of your letter of April 15th, 1943, setting forth a proposal relative to the transfer to the Government (through Rubber Reserve Company) of Buna patent rights which form the basis of the national synthetic rubber program under a plan as therein outlined.

Your proposal is, I feel, very definitely in the public interest, and this is an eminently propitious time to make this offer. Plants to make raw materials for synthetic rubber are coming into production. Two of the so-called "standard design" copolymer plants for the manufacture of Buna-S have made synthetic rubber of better quality than was, until recently, thought possible. However, there are uses for which the present-day synthetic rubber does not fully replace crude rubber, and it is not the way of American scientists or American industry to be content with today's quality. The synthetic rubbers of the future will be of better and better quality. It is appropriate that everything possible be done to hasten this improvement.

It is with the above in mind that I understand you are now proposing a constructive plan under which you give up for the benefit of the entire nation your right to collect royalties under basic Buna rubber patents, and it is for this same reason that I expect to see the Government continue an extensive research program in the rubber field.

Your proposal provides the necessary foundation for a general plan of free licenses under the patent rights of all American industry directly bearing on a very important part of our program, and I earnestly hope that your example will lead others to join promptly in this effort.

Sincerely yours,

(s) W. M. Jeffers

So far as the Government itself was concerned, this proposal meant that if it would spend $5,000,000 for research in the synthetic rubber field, it would not have to pay anyone any royalties. So far as industry was concerned, it meant that anyone could have a free license under all the synthetic rubber patents involved if he would cooperate in the war rubber program and grant free licenses under his own patents to the government and all other cooperators.*

The proposal was accepted by the stockholders of Standard Oil Co. (N.J.) at their annual meeting on June 1, 1943, and was put into effect on August 4, 1943, by the execution of an agreement between Standard and Rubber Reserve. This same agreement was offered by the government to all the companies actively interested in the synthetic rubber development, and was accepted by virtually the entire rubber industry. The effect of these agreements was that the basic industry of manufacturing the Buna type synthetic rubber for tires and general use could be conducted in the postwar world on the freest competitive basis without payment of royalties to anyone.

Probably the strongest objection to this agreement was that it tended to reduce the incentive for private research. This was not only because the private research worker found himself in competition with the $5,000,000 government research program but also because there could be no patent monopoly and no royalties under any inventions which are "Buna patent rights which form the basis of the national synthetic rubber program." This field of cooperation and cross-licensing for the period of the war included Buna-S rubber and all other types of Buna or similar rubbers containing 50 per cent or more of products of the nature of butadiene and which were useful for tires and other general purposes.

To minimize this tendency to reduce the incentive for private research, it seemed to everyone that specialty rubbers should be exempted and this reservation was incorporated in the agreement. The specialty rubbers, or rubbers useful mainly for special purposes, sell at relatively high prices and

---

* The unsolved legal question of the rights of the A.P.C. was settled quite simply, through his cooperation, by the grant through Rubber Reserve, of a general free license by the A.P.C. under any and all synthetic rubber patent rights owned by him. If it should be eventually decided that A.P.C., not Standard, owned some or all of the German originated patents, this grant would take effect and all parties would be protected.

constitute a normal field of competitive commercial endeavor, a field which was developed entirely without Governmental assistance. It might fairly be said that the necessary governmental intervention in the basic rubber field was a blight rather than an aid to the development of specialty rubbers. This distinction between the basic industry and the specialty industry was carried through into the exchange of licenses and of information about the compounding of the synthetic rubber. Specialty rubber was thus definitely segregated from the field of national interest. The free play of incentive and of the profit motive as encouragement for research was left to operate in the field of specialty types of synthetic rubber such as Buna-N and the many similar products of this character in which there had been a growing private business.

The satisfactory working out of this industry-wide program for cooperation and cross-licensing in aid of the Government's emergency production of Buna-S rubber, came to fruition just as the first of the government-owned plants under the control of the Rubber Director went into successful operation. It was accepted as a fitting climax of the work of the Rubber Director's office, and as the best possible foundation for a healthy synthetic rubber industry following the war.

CHAPTER XX

THE NEW INDUSTRY

The crisis in the struggle to establish the synthetic rubber industry was reached during the first half of 1943. At the beginning of the year there were troubles, delays and uncertainties on every front of the enormous and complex program. By mid-year the important plant designs had all proved satisfactory, the first great units were in successful operation, turning out butadiene, styrene and Buna-S rubber at rates above their designed capacity, and the tire makers had started to deliver good tires made of the Buna-S.

The effort by the technical and construction organizations of American industry which had been involved in pushing through to this initial success was beyond any detailed description. It represented an industrial achievement in planning, coordination and execution, comparable with the military achievement of "D" Day in Normandy. Both were without precedent for the combination of magnitude and complexity which they represented. Both were vital to the winning of the war, and both succeeded with a margin of reserve strength but no margin of time. Each represented, however, only the successful beginning of a hard campaign.

From the black days of Pearl Harbor it had taken eighteen months to begin making synthetic rubber successfully on the scale required. It required thirty months to push forward to final victory. Only in the second quarter of 1944 did synthetic rubber production catch up with demand.

Running true to his own definition of his personal responsibilities, Mr. Jeffers resigned as Rubber Director in the late summer of 1943 and turned over the reins to Colonel Dewey, who was at once appointed to succeed him. Mr. Jeffers had completed his task as leader of the assault force, had established a beach-head of initial success, and safety landed his organization on the firm ground of public confidence.

In the succeeding year Colonel Dewey drove to completion the entire program of fifty-one great primary plants, representing a total direct cost borne by the government of more than $700,000,000 and very large indirect costs borne by private industry.

The final report of the Rubber Director (Report No. 6 of July 25, 1944) gave a statistical summary of the primary manufacturing plants and their operations. This summary * shows an industry centered in three areas—the Northeast, ranging from Louisville, Kentucky to Naugatuck, Connecticut, and Sarnia, Ontario; the Southwest, made up of the States of Louisiana and Texas; and the Pacific, concentrated around Los Angeles. Approximately two-thirds of the industry is shown as based on petroleum, one-third on alcohol.

On July 25, 1944, Colonel Dewey in turn forwarded his final report and his letter of resignation, recommending that the office of Rubber Director be abolished and its emergency powers given back to the regular agencies of government. This was the first instance of a self-planned dissolution by a great war agency.

The final phase of the creation of the new industry, the actual building of the plants, went into high gear with the appointment of the Baruch Committee on August 6, 1942. It ended two years later with the successful completion of the emergency construction task and the voluntary dissolution of the governmental machine which had been created to carry it through. From Baruch to Jeffers to Dewey became an historic triple play which in the last inning had won the most critical of all the games on the home field.

* Appendix, p. 297.

The American synthetic rubber industry was primarily the creation of the chemical engineer. It is the chemical engineer who has given modern oil and chemical industries the equivalent of the mass production techniques of our mechanical industries. As the name implies, this relatively new profession is a marriage of the pure science of chemistry with the applied sciences of engineering. It is the chemical engineer who takes over the discoveries of the research chemist and carries the main load of development in the chemical industries. In this new profession the United States has been the leader. It is difficult for any race or nation to claim, over any long period, pre-eminence in any branch of science. But twenty-five years of intimate contact with the industrial science of Europe left this observer with the conviction that in chemical engineering America has had no close second. This conclusion was confirmed by the data on synthetic rubber obtained from Russia during the war and from Germany at the end of the war.

The Russian synthetic rubber industry, while much older than our own, was not so far advanced. No technique of Russian origin which seemed of value in the U.S. program ever became known to us, and on the other hand, Russia had needed, and obtained, with the approval of the Rubber Director and the Department of State, a license to manufacture du Pont's neoprene type of rubber and to produce alcohol from petroleum by Standard's processes, in order to make more of the Buna type rubber without further reducing its edible grain supplies.

The main American rubber program had been based on the prewar German chemical research on Buna-S rubber, and it was to be expected that Germany would continue to progress in both the chemical and chemical engineering aspects of the Buna industry. The German records which were examined at the end of the war showed that in some minor particulars they had made further progress on the chemical side. But on the coordination of Buna-S quality with tire manufacturing requirements, and on the large-scale production of the butadiene and styrene and of the Buna-S rubber itself, the American chemical engineers and chemists were in the lead.

On December 8, 1943, the biennial "Award for Chemical Engineering Achievement" which had been established in 1933 by the professional journal "Chemical and Metallurgical Engineering" for the encouragement of this most recent of the great engineering professions, was awarded to "The American Synthetic Rubber Industry" as represented by some 65 * companies who had contributed to the building of the new industry.

The end of the war found the new industry running smoothly, ready and able to supply the world's shortage of rubber during the long period required to restore natural rubber production in the Far East. To the credit of the industry for its role during the war, there must be added the credit for speeding the world's reconstruction effort.

In these emergency roles the value of the industry was incalculable. Nor is it possible to fix any exact value on its possible future role as an element in the permanent defense of the nation. But aside from these considerations, the industry can be evaluated in economic terms.

Two types of economic evaluation may be made. The first type is an evaluation of the fundamental economics of synthetic rubber production. To make this evaluation we need to know the basic relations between the new industry and our national economy as a whole. To arrive at this it is helpful to turn to Canada.

The Canadian Government decided on the outbreak of war in the Pacific to create a national synthetic rubber industry sufficient for Canada's needs and for this purpose set up a Crown Company called Polymer Corporation, Ltd. Polymer Corporation established close working relations with the Rubber Reserve Company of the United States and from early

* List in Appendix, p. 300.

1942 the Canadian rubber program was worked out as an autonomous division of a combined American program. In Canada there were installed Buna-S production facilities having a rated capacity of 30,000 tons and Butyl facilities rated at 7000 tons.

The Canadian development was carried out as an integrated operation on a site adjoining the largest Canadian oil refinery at Sarnia,* Ontario. The petroleum gases from which the butadiene is produced, and containing also the isobutylene for Butyl rubber and the ethylene for styrene manufacture, are delivered to this site by pipeline from the adjacent refinery. Coal, handled by the latest mechanical equipment, is used for fuel. All separations and conversions are carried out as a part of the integrated rubber operation and the residue gases are returned to the refinery. There is also provided, as a part of the rubber development, electric power, steam, water supply and all other public service facilities, including roads and railroad trackage and, in addition, shops, warehouses, laboratories, medical and restaurant facilities; in short, everything that goes to make up a complete industrial development.

Sarnia is therefore one point at which a complete national synthetic rubber industry with all of its important component and tributary facilities is self-sufficient and is centered at a single location. In the United States and Germany the complex fabric of the new industry was to a greater or less extent subdivided and interwoven into the pre-existing fabrics of other industries. No comparable data are available from Russia. Examination of this Canadian cross section, therefore, supplies most conveniently the basic figures on the economics of the industry.

First, as to capital cost, the Canadian figures check well enough with the American figures of about $1000 per ton of rated annual capacity, when allowance is made for the indi-

---

* This refinery belongs to Imperial Oil Company, the Canadian affiliate of Standard Oil Company (N.J.).

rect investment and private investment not reflected by the
official American figures. Second, as to the employees required, the Canadian plant requires about 1900 employees for
all purposes and all functions. This would indicate an average
production at rated capacity of about 21 long tons of synthetic rubber per year for each employee, including not only
production employees but also clerical, professional and service staffs of all kinds. With each employee turning out at least
21 long tons per annum the total labor cost is not more than
about 5 cents per pound. Third, as to raw materials. The
Canadian figures indicate that the consumption of basic raw
material is about 2 pounds of refinery gas and about 10.5
pounds of coal for each pound of rubber produced. The
other raw materials are inconsequential.* With the aid of
these Canadian figures, the fundamental economics of the new
industry can be reduced to these terms.

First, the capital cost of the industry was probably something less than one-half of one per cent of the national income
during the two-year period of construction. On a fifteen-year
life basis for the plants this means that to provide and replace
the plant used by the industry would require one-fifteenth of
one per cent of the national income. To keep the industry
running requires about the same fraction of total employment.
Of the basic natural resources, coal and oil, the U. S. would
consume in rubber production roughly one-half of one per
cent of our total current consumption for all purposes, on
the basis of these Canadian statistics.

There is a surprising concordance in the figures on the
fundamental economics of the new industry. Its requirements
for capital, labor, and natural resources are all consistent and
all a satisfactorily small part of the national total.

In the actual synthetic rubber industry of the United States,
these fundamental economics are more difficult to determine,

---

* About ⅕ pound of benzol is used in making the styrene for each
pound of rubber.

both because the industry is interwoven with older industrial installations and because oil and natural gas have been substituted in part for coal as fuel and alcohol has been substituted in part for hydrocarbon gas as a raw material. But these substitutions, to the extent they are made, are of special advantage for some reason and therefore do not affect the validity of the basic figures.

The second type of economic evaluation of the new industry is the simple one of relative costs. Does the synthetic rubber cost more or less, in terms of dollars, than natural rubber?

The actual price range, f.o.b. New York of No. 1 ribbed smoked sheets—the standard grade of natural rubber—has been as low as 2 cents and as high as $1.15. Even since the establishment of the International Rubber Agreement in 1934, it has been as low as 9.9 cents and as high as 23 * cents.

The estimated peace-time cost of Buna-S, the standard grade synthetic rubber, is in the range of 15 cents to 20 cents a pound. These costs can be realized when using either petroleum gases or alcohol as raw material, provided the alcohol is the cheapest possible industrial alcohol. The cost estimates of 15 cents to 20 cents a pound for the basic Buna-S type of synthetic rubber differ mainly in the assumptions made as to future prices of raw materials and labor rates and the provision made for amortization and interest in capital.

In the realm of dollar economics as in the realm of fundamental economics the new industry seems therefore to be a sound one, with production costs within the ordinary range of prices paid for imported rubber, and below the average prices in the immediate prewar years.

To complete the portrait of the new industry it is necessary to turn for a moment to the complex question of rubber quality. The principal grade of natural rubber is made from the latex of Hevea Brasiliensis, the tree which covers the Far East-

* Post-war prices exceeded 27 cents.

ern plantations. But there are many grades, quality differentials and price differentials. Natural rubbers of noticeably different characters are also produced commercially, although on a small scale as yet, from other plants. In America the major development has been that of the guayule bush, a native of Mexico. In Russia the major source of natural rubber is the kok-sagys or Russian dandelion. In Africa it is the cryptostegia vine.

In the synthetic rubber field the basic product of the new industry, representing 86 per cent of the total production,* is Buna-S. But there are also Buna-N, neoprene, Thiokol, and the newcomer, Butyl; and each of these types already developed is susceptible of innumerable variations.

To the rubber fabricating industry which consumes all these products in the manufacture of tires, tubes, mechanical rubber goods, surgical rubber goods, clothing, boots and shoes and countless other items, each type or grade of natural or synthetic rubber is a different problem and a new opportunity. Rubber is used in its pure form in only a minute percentage of the business. Almost always it is compounded or mixed with other substances such as carbon black, oil, glue, fibers, pigments and other plastics, including reclaimed rubber which is quite cheap and has in itself very desirable properties.

The value of the rubber article which the consumer buys, whether it be a tire or a hot water bottle, depends not only upon the type of rubber used by the manufacturer but also on the skill which he has used in blending it with the other required components, and the mechanical design of the article. What kind of a tread does the tire have? How thick is the side wall? What fabric is used in the carcass? All of these variables are interdependent. If one is changed, the others must be experimented with to see whether a better final product can be made.

So it follows that the synthetic rubbers present endless new

* At the end of the war. This reflects full capacity of all plants.

problems and possibilities. One can speak of quality only in general terms. In these generalities the status of the new industry at the time of its establishment was that synthetic rubber had been substituted successfully for all grades of natural rubber to the extent of 85 per cent of the total rubber requirements of the United States and Canada. In some cases the synthetic rubber article was slightly better, in some cases slightly worse, but by and large this difference was indistinguishable save to the expert. Time and experience, the progressive improvement of the synthetic rubber, and changes in compounding and in the mechanical design of rubber articles will produce an ever-changing panorama of constructive competition between the natural and synthetic rubbers.

There are a few fundamental differences between the various rubbers which indicate the main lines of this competition. It has proved very difficult to approach the best grades of natural rubber in their low internal friction or hysteresis, and for this reason tire carcasses which tend to heat up badly in service such as the large, thick, truck and bus tires for cross-country service, are still a preferred outlet for natural rubber.

On the other hand it has been found possible to obtain for Buna-S synthetic rubbers resistance to abrasion or wear and road grip on wet roads better than that of natural rubber and it may be expected that tire treads for ordinary passenger car service will probably be a preferred outlet for this synthetic rubber. For tubes, the Butyl synthetic rubber has the advantage of holding the air pressure very much better and also greater resistance to tearing which reduces the danger from punctures at high speed. For resistance to sunlight, to oil, and to attack by chemicals, the synthetics neoprene, thiokol and the various Buna-N types are already far ahead, each one excelling in one respect or another.

It seems inevitable that in the future the competitive race on details of quality will be won more and more often by these and other synthetic products, and that the main competition will then be on price. For a very large part of the total rubber market—perhaps more than three-fourths of it—the probable quality differences are not apt to be controlling as against the price differentials which unrestricted competition between natural and synthetic rubber may produce.

In synthetic rubber, the nation has created a great industry. It did not come into being without birth pains. This story of the birth of the industry, incomplete in many details, may nevertheless be adequate as a case history to illustrate the way in which our American society actually operated in peace and in war to create new industries and advance old ones.

APPENDIX

AGREEMENT made and entered into this 9th day of November 1929 by and between:

I. G. FARBENINDUSTRIE AKTIENGESELLSCHAFT, a German corporation, of Frankfurt am Main, Germany, hereinafter referred to as "I. G.," and

STANDARD OIL COMPANY, a corporation incorporated under the laws of the State of New Jersey, hereinafter referred to as "the Company."

WHEREAS I. G. and the Company are two of the four parties named in the agreement of even date herewith, a copy of which is annexed hereto, and the terms of which require close cooperation between I. G. and the Company, along technical lines; and

WHEREAS the Company recognizes the preferred position of I. G. in the industries known as chemical, and I. G. recognizes the preferred position of the Company in the industries known as oil and natural gas, and

WHEREAS neither party has any plan or policy of so far expanding its existing business in the direction of the other party's industry as to become a serious competitor of that other party, but each recognizes that certain overlapping of activities will exist;

Now, THEREFORE, with a view to preventing such overlap from becoming a source of mutual irritation and unwillingness to cooperate on technical lines as is required under said four-party agreement, the parties hereto have agreed that their policies shall be as follows:

ARTICLE I. NEW CHEMICAL DEVELOPMENTS BY THE COMPANY

If the Company shall desire to initiate anywhere in the world a new chemical development not closely related to its then business, it will offer to I. G. control of such new enterprise (including the patent rights thereto) on fair and reasonable terms.

Examples. a. A development not related at all is the production of artificial silk by present methods.

b. A development related but not closely related is the production of nonhydrocarbon solvents from natural gas.

Article II. New Chemical Developments by I. G.

1. If I. G. shall desire to initiate outside of Germany (as "Germany" is defined in Article XIV of said four-party agreement) a new chemical development which cannot be advantageously carried on except as a department of an oil or natural gas business, it will offer control thereof (including the patent rights thereto) to the Company on fair and reasonable terms.

Examples. a. The production of solvents, whether hydrocarbon or nonhydrocarbon, from olefines produced in refining oils.

b. The production of an antiknock compound to the extent that the same shall be sold to or through oil companies.

2. If I. G. shall desire to initiate outside of Germany (as "Germany" is defined in Article XIV of said four-party agreement) a new chemical development not covered by subparagraph 1 of this Article but related to the then business of the Company, as for example by use of natural gas or petroleum products, I. G. will offer to the Company a substantial but not controlling participation.

Examples: a. The production of fixed nitrogen from natural gas.

b. The production of acetylene from natural or refinery gas.

Article III. Duration of This Agreement

This agreement shall continue in force throughout the duration of said four-party agreement and no longer.

Article IV. Subsidiaries

This agreement shall be binding upon and inure to the benefit of the subsidiaries of the respective parties hereto as provided in Article XIII of said four-party agreement, to the same extent as if said Article were incorporated in this agreement, it being understood that no subsidiary corporation of the character referred to in paragraph B of said Article XIII shall have the privilege of ratifying either the four-party agreement or this agreement without also ratifying the other.

IN WITNESS WHEREOF the parties hereto have set their hands and seals on the day and year first above mentioned.

I. G. FARBENINDUSTRIE AKTIENGESELLSCHAFT,

By [signed] SCHMITZ V. KNIERIEM.

Attest:

STANDARD OIL COMPANY (N. J.),

By [signed] W. C. TEAGLE.

[SEAL]

AGREEMENT

between

I.G. Farbenindustrie Aktiengesellschaft

and

Standard Oil Development Company

The parties to this agreement are I.G. Farbenindustrie Aktiengesellschaft, a German corporation, hereinafter called I.G., and Standard Oil Development Company, a corporation of Delaware, hereinafter called Standard.

Wherever the term "new chemical process" is used in this agreement it means a process which comes within all of the following limitations:

A. It shall employ as starting material crude petroleum, natural bitumen or natural gas or products made therefrom, to the extent only that they are made therefrom, and it shall be complete in the sense that it produces a marketable product. Wherever the production of further products from the first marketable product obtained shall be a natural and logical development of the production of the first marketable product rather than an incident to the existing business of the parties, the production of such further products, shall be likewise included subject always to the limitations B, C and D.

B. It shall be a chemical process of a nature different from the separation and refining of petroleum and natural gas.

C. It shall be a process not coming within a certain four-party agreement of November 9th, 1929, to which I.G. and Standard Oil Company (New Jersey) are parties.

D. It shall not have been commercially used by either party prior to the date of this agreement.

It is the desire and intention of the parties to develop and exploit their new chemical processes jointly on a basis of equality (50-50) and they therefore obligate themselves to proceed as follows:

ARTICLE I.

There shall be organized immediately under the laws of a State of the United States a corporation hereinafter called the JOINT COMPANY. The initial cash capital of the JOINT COMPANY shall be $800,000. which shall be raised by the sale of its common stock to the parties in equal amounts at the same price. The capital investment and the number of employees of the JOINT COMPANY will be held to the minimum limits compatible with the proper conduct of its business especially by the following procedure: The operations of the Joint Company will be confined as nearly as practicable to the investigation, testing, development and licensing of new chemical processes brought to it by the parties. The procedure in each case is to be determined only as the case arises but commercial use by the JOINT COMPANY itself of the new chemical processes brought to it will be in the main confined to the initial or temporary operations required to demonstrate the process. Larger scale permanent operations are expected to be carried on by licensing the process to established manufacturers able to employ it, or by forming new companies in which the parties and/or the JOINT COMPANY will become interested.

Technical employees, executives and specialists in the employ of the parties will be asigned to perform services connected with the work of the JOINT COMPANY while remaining employees of the parties respectively, and the JOINT COMPANY will reimburse the party in question for the reasonable cost to it of the services so rendered. Technical employees of the parties performing services for the JOINT COMPANY will in all cases be bound by contract to assign their inventions to their respective employers to the end that such inventions may be brought within this agreement, to the extent to which they come within its terms, by the employer. THE JOINT COMPANY will buy or lease the required land and erect and own the equipment used in its operations. By agreement of the parties wherever it is convenient and economically desirable to do so one of the parties may arrange for the conduct of the operations of the JOINT COMPANY, for its account, and at cost, by the party or a subsidiary which is in an advantageous position to carry on such work.

For the purpose of carrying on the first operations of the JOINT COMPANY it is contemplated that the most favorable location will be a site within the Baton Rouge refinery. It is also contemplated that these first operations will require extensive and important interconnections with other operations carried on in this refinery, and the frequent use of laboratory and other equipment located outside of the site of the JOINT COMPANY operations.

For the above reasons it is deemed desirable that the operations of the JOINT COMPANY which are immediately contemplated shall be carried on under the financial and technical direction of the JOINT COMPANY by STANDARD, the latter arranging for the construction and operation of the equipment wanted by the JOINT COMPANY with the Standard Oil Company of Louisiana. Accordingly, the procedure will be for the JOINT COMPANY to request STANDARD to cause to be erected on the agreed upon site at Baton Rouge such equipment as the JOINT COMPANY shall require. The The JOINT COMPANY will assume entire control of and responsibility for the designs and specifications of such equipment, and complete financial and technical supervision over the purchase, fabrication, erection and operation thereof and the sale for its account of products made. These functions it will exercise through its administrative officers and through technical representatives detailed by the parties to Baton Rouge for that purpose. The actual operations and purchase, fabrication and erection will, however, be carried on by Standard Oil Company of Louisiana, and the title to the equipment will be in that Company. The JOINT COMPANY will reimburse STANDARD currently for all expenditures either for equipment or operations made by Standard Oil Company of Louisiana under the direction of STANDARD, but under directions of the JOINT COMPANY such equipment will be at any time sold or otherwise disposed of and the net proceeds of such disposition paid to the JOINT COMPANY.

The representatives of the parties shall agree upon the accounting practice to be used by Standard Oil Company of Louisiana in arriving at the cost of services, operations and equipment which the JOINT COMPANY is obligated to pay for. It is understood that in arriving at such cost there shall be no interest charge on account of equipment used. Electric energy and similar services shall be charged at average cost so long as the quantities required do not cause Standard Oil Company of Louisiana to exceed the limitations of existing facilities or the minimum rate clauses of existing contracts such as the Louisiana Steam Products contract of October 15, 1929. For quantities in excess of such amounts the cost charged shall be the actual cost of providing or supplying the excess quantity.

ARTICLE II.

As soon as either party shall have developed a new chemical process which it is then free to assign to the JOINT COMPANY under the provisions of Article III hereof, it shall acquaint the other party with all technical and commercial details thereof and give the other party an option, exercisable within four months, to elect whether the process in question shall be further investigated, tested and developed by the JOINT COMPANY. If within the said four months the other party shall elect not to request that the process be so investigated, tested and developed by the JOINT COMPANY, then the process in question shall be thereafter free of the operation of this agreement. If within the said four months the other party so requests, the JOINT COMPANY shall undertake the investigation, testing and further development of the process, and the originating party in the first instance and the other party as well to the extent possible for it, shall be bound to assist the JOINT COMPANY in all ways in such work, and especially by providing technical and trade information and experienced technical experts for carrying on the work.

ARTICLE III.

If and when the investigation, testing and further development of any new chemical process by the JOINT COMPANY shall have proceeded to the extent that commercial exploitation is in order, the parties shall grant to the JOINT COMPANY suitable exclusive licenses or licensing rights (excluding also the grantor) under their existing and future patent rights, including experience, for the world outside of Germany, to the extent they are not precluded from so doing by contracts with others in force on the date of such grant.

The parties will endeavor to keep one another advised as to any contracts they may have or enter into which may directly, definitely, and for a long term, preclude them from assigning any patent rights to the JOINT COMPANY as herein provided, and to the extent to which either party is precluded from so assigning, to that same extent the other party shall be free from the obligations of this Article.

It is understood that under the terms of the preceding paragraphs it remains possible for each party to enter into agreements with others which may bear upon or even include directly processes which must be later offered to the JOINT COMPANY or which are at the time actually under investigation, testing and development by the JOINT COMPANY. This freedom is deemed necessary to the conduct of the regular businesses of the parties and is desirable for the purposes of this agreement in that it permits of the maximum latitude of technical cooperation and enlarges the opportunities of the JOINT COMPANY. The parties will, however, be governed by their intention to accomplish the purpose of this agreement in exercising the freedom of action which they have under the preceding paragraphs of this Article.

As a condition precedent to the grant of exclusive licensing rights to the JOINT COMPANY, agreement between the parties on the following points is required:

A. A definition of the process in question.

B. Whether the originating party shall be entitled to the entire 25% royalty as provided in Article IV-H, or whether the other party is entitled to a portion of such royalty under Article V-C and D.

C. Which party is to have the deciding voice in the future management of the exploitation of the process under Article VII.

D. What disposition can be made of any existing contractual obligations of either party bearing upon the process.

E. How the existing marketing organizations and facilities of the parties may be most advantageously used in connection with the marketing of the product of the process.

ARTICLE IV.

A. The JOINT COMPANY shall keep the usual books of account for the operations of the JOINT COMPANY as a whole.

B. In addition the JOINT COMPANY shall keep separate accounts for each new chemical process as to which it incurs expenses, or from which it derives revenue, each such separate account to show as nearly as may be practicable the net income or net loss to date resulting from its operations relating to that process.

C. From the general books of account kept under Paragraph "A" above, there shall be determined for each calendar year the amount earned for that year applicable to the payment of dividends on the common stock.

D. There shall also be determined for the same period and in the same way as in "C" above, the average investment of the company actually employed in the conduct of its business, which shall be taken as the mean of such investments for the beginning and end of the year in question.

E. From the annual earnings as determined in Paragraph "C" above, there shall be deducted an amount sufficient to give a 20% cumulative return on the average investment as determined in "D" above.

F. From the separate accounts kept in accordance with Paragraph "B", it shall be determined which new chemical processes have showed a net profit from the time when the first expenditures were made thereon until the end of the year in question. These shall be called the profitable processes. The aggregate profit, for the year in question, of all of the profitable processes shall be then determined from the said accounts of Paragraph "B". The amount remaining after the deduction of Paragraph "E" above, shall be divided by the aggregate profit thus determined, and the quotient called the net process income factor.

EXAMPLE: The aggregate profit for the year 1935 of all the profitable processes is 100. The income for the year, as determined by Paragraph "C", with the deduction of Paragraph "E", is 80. The net process income factor is 80/100 or 0.8.

G. From the separate accounts kept in accordance with Paragraph "B", there shall be determined the net profit for each profitable process for the year in question, which amount shall then be multiplied by the net process income factor as determined in Paragraph "F". The result shall be called the final net process income for the process in question for the year in question.

EXAMPLE: There are two profitable processes for and as of the year 1935. Process A shows a net profit of 70, process B, 30. Multiplying each by the net process income factor, 0.8, the final net process income of process A for 1935 is 56, and of process B, 24.

H. Out of any final net process income determined in accordance with Paragraph "G" above, the JOINT COMPANY shall pay to the party originating the process in question, annually, and as soon as the completion of the accounting shall have shown the amount payable, 25% of such final net process income for the process in question for the year in question. Such payments shall be made for and on account of each calendar year including that in which the process in question was first commercially exploited through the JOINT COMPANY, and thereafter until and including the year 1947, regardless of whether this agreement as a whole shall terminate earlier or later.

ARTICLE V.

A. The rule shall be that the party which first acquaints the other with the technical details of a new chemical process, under the terms of Article II shall be considered the originator of that process for the purposes of Article IV-H.

B. The rule shall be also that there shall be no reduction of the compensation paid to the originating party under Article IV-H because of improvements made by the other party after the date of the first disclosure under Article II.

C. In cases in which both parties have important patent rights relating to the same new chemical process at the time of its first disclosure under Article II, the rule of Paragraph A of this Article shall be modified as may be required to work fairly.

D. In cases in which very important improvements are made in the new chemical process after the date of first disclosure under Article II by the party not originating the process, the rule of Paragraph B shall be modified as may be required to work fairly.

ARTICLE VI.

Since all technical employees of the JOINT COMPANY remain employees of the respective parties, the inventions made by such employees go to their respective employers and from there to the JOINT COMPANY, to the extent to which they fall within this agreement. The same will be true with inventions made jointly by employees of both parties, each party obtaining the entire interest of its employee, which interest becomes subject to this agreement. To the extent to which the interest in question is not subject to this agreement it is specifically understood that either party shall have the right to use the inventions of such joint patent rights in any country, and to license the same, all without accounting to the other party, subject always to the provisions of the said four party agreement of November 9, 1929, and to a

certain agreement of the same date between the I.G. and Standard
Oil Company (New Jersey).

I.G. shall have a royalty free, divisible, transferable license, for
the full term of the patents, under any German patents of
STANDARD based upon inventions made by employees of STANDARD
who at the time of making such inventions shall be engaged in
performing services for the JOINT COMPANY, except that if such
inventions relate to the Hydrocarbon field as the same is defined
in the said four-party agreement of November 9, 1929, then I.G.
shall have instead the same license under STANDARD's German patents which is granted to it under said four-party agreement.

ARTICLE VII.

The parties shall try to come to agreement on all matters having to do with the handling of new chemical processes brought to
the JOINT COMPANY but in case of failure of agreement the decision shall rest with the party which would have been entitled to
the control of the process under a certain agreement of November 9, 1929 between I.G. and Standard Oil Company (New
Jersey), but the controlling party shall not be relieved of the
obligation to forward the interests of the JOINT COMPANY rather
than its own interest where the two conflict.

ARTICLE VIII.

For the purposes of this agreement "Germany" means the territory to which German patents now apply.

ARTICLE IX.

This agreement shall remain in force until terminated by two
years written notice served by one party upon the other, but no
such notice shall be served prior to December 31, 1945.

ARTICLE X.

The parties desire to record in the text of this agreement the
fact that, with entire willingness on both sides to enter into fully
defined and binding obligations relating to the subject matter
hereof, they have found it impossible to accomplish this purpose

in full, and have been compelled in part to substitute agreement as to order and principles of procedure in making future specific agreements.

IN WITNESS WHEREOF, the parties hereto have caused this agreement to be executed in triplicate by their officers thereunto duly authorized this 30th day of September 1930.

In so doing the parties hereto, and also the Standard Oil Company (New Jersey) owner of 100% of the capital stock of STANDARD, agree that in the event any corporation or corporations which within the life of this agreement shall be in effect the sole owner of, or the sole property of, or the sole property of the sole owner of I.G. or Standard Oil Company (New Jersey) shall fail to subscribe hereto or to comply with the terms hereof, then I.G. or Standard Oil Company (New Jersey) will indemnify and hold harmless the other against any and all consequences of such failure.

I.G. FARBENINDUSTRIE AKTIENGESELLSCHAFT.
GREIF

ppa HOCHSCHWENDER

STANDARD OIL DEVELOPMENT COMPANY.
FRANK A. HOWARD
Vice-President.

Attest:
M. H. EAMES
Secretary.

STANDARD OIL COMPANY (NEW JERSEY)
E. M. CLARK
Vice-President.

Attest:
C. T. WHITE
Secretary.

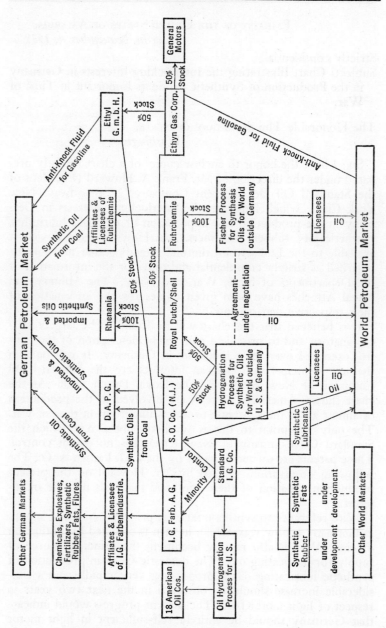

1938 REPORT ON FOREIGN INTERESTS IN GERMAN
SYNTHETIC PROCESSES

EMBASSY OF THE UNITED STATES OF AMERICA,
Berlin, November 4, 1938.

Strictly confidential.

Subject: Chart Illustrating the Interlocking Interests in Germany in the Production of Synthetic Products Important in Time of War.

The Honorable The SECRETARY OF STATE,
Washington.

SIR: I have the honor to enclose copies of a chart recently prepared under the direction of Mr. Frank A. Howard (President of the Standard Oil Development Company, 26 Broadway, New York City), which illustrates the interlocking interests in Germany in the production and importation of oil fuels, lubricants, synthetic fats, rubber, and fibers. Mr. Howard made this chart available to the Embassy on the understanding that it would be regarded as strictly confidential and only for the information of the Departments of State, War, and Navy. The Military and Naval Attachés have been given copies for the information of their respective departments.

It is believed that the chart will be found to be largely self-explanatory and to provide a convenient description of the control exercised over these industries in Germany. It will be seen that the principal non-German interests are the Standard Oil Company of New Jersey and the Royal Dutch Shell. As the chart shows, American interests are involved in the production of almost all of the synthetic products important in time of war. The only exception to this is synthetic fiber, over which the Standard Oil Company of New Jersey has no patent control. These patents are owned outright by the I. G. Farben A. G. The following observations offered by Mr. Howard on the present production situation of these synthetic materials may be of interest:

With reference to synthetic fats, the principal source of supply in Germany is now wax, which in turn is obtained by distillation of coal. Wax is also rapidly becoming the principal source of supply for lubricating oils. The domestic German production of synthetic lubricating oils is progressing very rapidly and a considerable increase should be observed in the next two years in respect of light motor fuel. The present progress would indicate that Germany should be entirely self-sufficient in light motor fuels by 1941. This estimate, of course, takes into account the domestic production of natural petroleum, benzol, and alcohol-menthol. The production of industrial fats is expected to increase rapidly in the next few years. It is hoped that the synthetic production of fats obtained from coal will eventually be increased to a level sufficient to cover all industrial requirements, thereby liberating animal fats for edible purposes.

Respectfully yours,

(Signed) HUGH R. WILSON.
Hugh R. Wilson.

(Enclosure: 1. Chart, as above.)

STANDARD OIL COMPANY (NEW JERSEY)

EXTRACT FROM EXECUTIVE COMMITTEE MEMORANDUM
OCTOBER 31, 1938

"*Synthetic Rubber.* Negotiations indicate that the German Government will now permit discussions of details with, and revelation of technical processes to non-German parties in interest, so that within one or two months considerable progress ought to be made in these negotiations; *although the German interests hope to sell the process to the international rubber cartel that course would probably mean the process might be buried in the interest of maintaining a market for natural rubber. From our approach, the possibility of interesting some rubber interest in the United States in a mutualized company for the commercialization of the process would seem the more normal course.* Although the base stock used in this synthetic process is normally refinery gas, there is a possibility of a less prolific supply by dehydrogenating the butane in natural gas. To the extent that the patent question has been searched to date, the situation seems clear of any major difficulty. . . ."

HAGUE AGREEMENT

MEMORANDUM RE READJUSTMENT OF JASCO

Whereas, under an agreement of September 30, 1930. I. G. and S. O. Dev. Co. agreed to cause to be originated a jointly owned corporation, to which they should assign certain patent rights, and whereas pursuant to said agreement there has been organized a corporation of Louisiana, under the name Jasco, and whereas it has been heretofore settled and agreed between the parties that Jasco is, pursuant to said agreement, the equitable owner of all patent rights of the parties relating to certain processes known as follows:

1. Paraffine Oxidation,
2. Acetylene Arc process,
3. Oppanol process,
4. Buna process,

and whereas the parties desire to readjust their respective rights to and in the said processes and in any other processes which shall come within the said agreement of September 30, 1930, it is agreed as follows:

I. I. G. agrees to assign and transfer to S. O. Dev. Co. all of I. G.'s rights, title, and interest in and to the stocks issued to it by and standing in its name on the books of the said corporation Jasco. It is understood that said stock is now held by Heidelbach Ikkelheimer & Co., of New York, as security for a loan of £40,000 —made by Hambros Bank Ltd., of London, to I. G., but I. G. will in due course regain said stock and deliver it to S. O. Dev. Co., and in the meantime S. O. Dev. Co. shall have record title, so that S. O. Dev. Co. may have the full right to vote said stocks and receive any dividends thereon. (Alternative, S. O. Dev. Co. to pay off the loan and take the stock.)

II. S. O. Dev. Co. agrees that it and Jasco will enter into a contract or contracts with I. G., substantially as follows:

I. G. assigns, quitclaims, and releases to Jasco all of I. G.'s rights, title, and interest in and to the royalties or payments to I. G., provided for in said agreement of September 30, 1930, between I. G. and S. O. Dev. Co., subject to which agreement and under the terms of which agreement Jasco has been the equitable owner of the processes heretofore listed.

In consideration of the said release and quitclaim of I. G. to Jasco, Jasco shall assign, release and quitclaim to I. G. all of Jasco's rights, title, and interest in and to the said processes for all countries of the world, except the United States of America, the British Empire, the French Empire (France, its colonies, possessions, protectorates, and mandates) and Iraq.

III. It is understood that each party intends to promote the said processes in the territory in which it has exclusive ownership thereof to the best of its ability but subject entirely to its own discretion.

IV. On request of either party (S. O. Dev. Co. or I. G.) made at any time after one year, and not more frequently than once each year thereafter, from the date hereof, the parties shall exchange reports of their respective returns from the promotion of the said processes, and if it shall appear from such reports that the division of territory of exclusive ownership between the parties as herein effected have not been equitable in its financial results as judged by the agreement of September 30, 1930, then the parties shall correct the inequity in such manner as may seem most fair and advantageous at the time.

Pursuant to the foregoing, I. G., S. O. Dev. Co., and Jasco shall make or cause to be made any formal assignments or execute any further instruments necessary to put into effect the present readjustment and any required future readjustment of the rights and interests of the parties to the agreement of September 30, 1930.

[Handwritten:] This is my original copy of this memorandum exchanged with Dr. Ringer at The Hague, Sept. 25, 1939.

FRANK A. HOWARD.

REPORT ON EUROPEAN TRIP

OCTOBER 12, 1939.

Mr. W. S. FARISH,
30 Rockefeller Plaza.

DEAR MR. FARISH: I left New York on the Clipper on August 16th with the intention of having a brief holiday in France and spending the month of September on business matters in Europe. The most important item of business was the consolidation of the I. H. P., Universal, Gasoline Products, Kellogg agencies for dealing with foreign patent rights in accordance with the plan worked out in the Long Beach meetings. In addition, I had the usual grist of contract and financial questions with the Shell and I. G. companies. Messrs. Carlisle and Asbury met me in Paris on August 21st, and after reviewing the Long Beach agreement with me they undertook to make the necessary preliminary studies during my holiday. I left for Vichy on August 22nd. Almost immediately after my arrival it appeared that war could not be avoided, and I therefore telegraphed you for instructions. Mr. Harden replied in your absence, agreeing with my suggestion that it probably would be best for me to remain and do what could be done, even at the risk of considerable delay in my return.

I stayed in France until September 17th—a small part of the time in Vichy, but mainly in Paris—being principally occupied during this time on various aspects of the French aviation supply problem. When these matters seemed on their way to a satisfactory solution I was able, through the kindness of M. de Monzie, the Minister concerned, to obtain permission to go to England at once. (Such permits were then normally obtainable only after two weeks' delay.) In England I met by appointment the Royal Dutch gentlemen from Holland, and after some days of discussions with them and with the Anglo-Iranian people a general agreement was reached on the necessary changes in our relations with the I. G., in view of the state of war. (It may here be noted that the position of the Royal Dutch Shell group is that it is essentially British and the activities of its Dutch as well as of its American components must conform to this view.) I also had several meetings with the representatives of the Air Ministry and endeavored to assist them in coordinating their program with the French program of aviation supplies.

In view of my close association with these supply problems, both in France and England, I was somewhat concerned about the impression which would be created when it was discovered that I had left these discussions to undertake discussions in Holland with Germans interested in the same problems. Both for this reason, and because I required help to obtain the necessary permission to go to Holland, I called on the counselor of our Embassy in London and explained the situation to him. He was extremely concerned about the matter, and very doubtful whether the Embassy could permit me to proceed with my plans. I had the impression at one stage that they were contemplating calling in my passport. After discussions with the Ambassador, however, the situation was cleared completely. It was agreed that I was entirely within my rights, and furthermore, that the Embassy would not only permit me to go, but would take the necessary steps to explain the situation to the British Foreign Office, in order to relieve me of all embarrassment and to facilitate my obtaining the required permits for leaving and reentering England. The gentlemen in the Air Ministry, who I think had a suspicion of the nature of my activities in Holland, also very kindly offered to assist me in reentering England, if the Foreign Office should make any difficulties about my return, since they stated they wanted to have a final discussion with me before I left for the U. S. In appreciation of this evidence of confidence, I offered, through the Embassy, to conduct all of my discussions in Holland in the presence of a member of the staff of the American Legation at The Hague. This was not required of me, however.

Pursuant to these arrangements I was able to keep my appointments in Holland, where I had three days of discussion with the representatives of the I. G. They delivered to me assignments of some 2,000 foreign patents and we did our best to work out complete plans for a modus vivendi which would operate through the term of the war, whether or not the U. S. came in. All of the arrangements could not be completed, but it is hoped that enough has been done to permit closing the most important uncompleted points by cable. It is difficult to visualize as yet just how successful we shall be in maintaining our relations through this period without personal contacts.

One serious difficulty which developed was the fact that the

French patent assignments were not legally complete because they lacked the certificate of the French Consulate in Berlin. Through my contact with the American Minister in The Hague I learned that our own Consulate had taken over the duties of the French Consulate. The French Ambassador at The Hague agreed that our German consular certificate would be accepted instead of the French consular certificate. At my request, the American minister at The Hague telegraphed Washington explaining this situation and asking permission to have the papers, after certification in Berlin by our Consulate, returned directly to Paris by the diplomatic courier, in order to avoid the difficulties and delays which would otherwise arise. Fortunately, the Department of State had in its files at Washington a full statement of our relations with the I. G. on these patent matters, which I had worked out with Ambassador Gibson in Berlin in September of 1938 and which had been forwarded by him to Washington. The necessary permission from the State Department was, therefore, obtained in about three days.

I returned to London through Belgium to minimize the length of the North Sea crossing.

On my return to London I had some further discussions with the Anglo-Iranian and Shell people concerning the I. G. patent problems, and also a final meeting with the gentlemen of the Air Ministry.

I returned from Foynes, Ireland, on October 9th after a delay of five days, awaiting departure of the Clipper. The life-insurance premium quoted in London for this last voyage of the northern Clipper was 2%.

The various specific items of business dealt with during my trip are being handled in the usual way with the persons directly concerned, or by separate memoranda. There seems to be no appropriate place except this letter, however, to bring up some matters of general interest.

The first is the position of our American personnel in England, France, and Holland. First, as to France, Mr. Crampton's family is well taken care of in Le Touquet in their summer house, and the only inconvenience they are apt to suffer is that they will probably have physicians or officers quartered in their home, since all hotels and available living space are required in Le Touquet for the large hospital services which have been centered there. Because of its remoteness, entirely residential character, and military use exclusively as a hospital center, there is no reason to believe that Le Touquet will suffer during the war. Messrs. Crampton and Irish are themselves remaining in Paris for the present. Messrs. Young and Meade are still living with their families adjacent to Port Jerome. This location is certainly not the best for the families.

In London, so far as I could learn, all of the families and wives of all the American group in the International Association, save Mrs. White, were able to get to the U. S. before or during the first week of the war. The men all have satisfactory suburban locations, although they are for the present spending much of their time in their usual London quarters. The strain of the initial weeks was rather bad, but the continued quiet has relieved much of this, and the health and spirits of the entire American personnel are quite good.

The principal source of worry of the American personnel, both in France and England, at the moment is the ultimate effect of the finance control of these countries on them, coupled with the natural fear that their business careers will be adversely affected by the war, whether it continues or not. The prospect of having no job left in Europe, or a relatively unimportant one, and the alternative of surrendering their American savings and income or deserting their jobs to escape the application of finance control, makes a rather disagreeable picture. Nevertheless, no one is unduly pessimistic, and although their business, like all of the business of the belligerent countries, is now being conducted at an unbelievably low level of efficiency, everyone is carrying on cheerfully with whatever work he can do.

There is a decided state of strain in Holland, although few people have deserted the country. Our personnel and their wives are all still on duty, although it was seen probable that Mr. Bolton, who is British, would have to be on active service.

In general, the only practical way of communication between the various European countries which is still left is by telegram. Telephone is prohibited, save for limited communication outward from France on ministerial priority order. The mails are not only delayed by the censorship, which of course applies to telegrams also, but are further delayed by the uncertainties of rail and sea communication. It often requires two weeks for a letter to reach Paris from London, or vice versa.

Travel is attended with all sorts of difficulties and delays and some real peril as regards the crossing of the North Sea and the Channel. Travel permits require from one to three weeks to obtain, and then only on good showing of real necessity and national interest. Train service on the Continent, even in Holland and Belgium, is still disorganized and under military control. Rail journeys that should require a few hours take an entire day. Channel and North Sea crossings are under the jurisdiction of the British Admiralty. Although the boats are fairly regular, they have no scheduled departure times and they move only in daylight. A daily air service has just opened between London and Paris, but up to this time it is restricted to government employees or other civilians traveling on government business.

Under the above conditions it is not possible even to attempt any coordination or central control of our European operations from London or any other point in Europe. So far as I know, during my stay in Europe, which covered the first six weeks of the war, there was not a single executive of any of the operating companies who moved out of his own country, nor any of the executives of the International Association group who attempted to make any direct contacts with the European markets, save on certain supply and shipping problems covered by telegraph.

I find myself in this report in the same difficulty which Ambassador Kennedy stated he found himself in, in trying to inform Washington on the situation. It is impossible in any report to really reflect the extent to which the industry and life of Europe has been affected by the threat of "total warfare," and by the universal reactions to this imminent threat.

From the standpoint of the Standard Oil Company (New Jersey) the most important thing which I would like to bring out is the seriousness of the financial and economic positions. Europe has already suffered injury to its economic life from which recovery is going to be terribly slow and difficult. The first place where the shoe is pinching already is the institution of complete financial controls in the belligerent countries, the effect of which will be to limit to the barest necessities of military and industrial life, the purchases of these countries which must be paid for in foreign exchange. Beyond this immediate effect, whether the war continues or not, there will be the result that the productive power of the belligerent countries for exportable goods is so seriously affected that this difficulty in securing foreign exchange will become at least a semi-permanent phenomenon, controlling all of their buying habits and internal life. The first effect will be that the oil consumption of the European markets may be materially reduced, or at least held far below the former rate of increase, for years to come. The second effect is that we shall be at a disadvantage as compared with our principal competitors, Anglo-Iranian and Shell, in supplying the military and commercial market which does exist, because they can utilize payment for their goods in sterling to a greater extent than ourselves.

We are apparently facing a real turning point in our foreign business. I discussed this matter at some length with the gentlemen in London, and I believe we are all in absolute agreement that the Jersey company must now reexamine its whole foreign business picture with a view to seeing how it can best orient itself to meet the problem of holding its own in impoverished markets, with very difficult exchange problems to meet, and against the increasing weight of more favorably located competition, and the probability of increasing government interference.

In this connection I commend to your consideration Mr. Porters' report to Mr. Crane of June 23rd.

The only ray of light discernible in this dark picture of the future of the European markets is in the possibility that necessity may drive Europe to the final adoption of some plan of federation, involving removal of customs barriers and unified industrial, financial, and foreign policies. There is quite a little talk on this matter in very influential circles at this time. The starting point of this talk is the fear that the present British-French war alliance is too weak to stand much strain. There is very real fear that the French government will either have to force England into an early peace on unsatisfactory terms, or find itself overthrown by French public opinion. To meet this pressing practical problem there is a thought of proposing to France the formation of a permanent federation with the U. K. It is recognized that such a plan might or might not be the starting point for a general federation of Western European states, along the Swiss model. Such a federation has, of course, been a dream solution of Europe's problems for a long time, but it obviously can get nowhere unless the foundation is laid by the dominant powers. A permanent French-British alliance, as a means of meeting the weakness of the present situation, might possibly supply the necessary foundation.

In any case, however, it seems that the problem of the Jersey company is to try to plan for itself the best possible course to meet problems which will be created by an impoverished Europe.

Very truly yours,

F. A. HOWARD.

FAH: MF

cc: Messrs. W. C. Teagle, Orville Harden, R. W. Gallagher, W. E. Pratt, F. H. Bedford, Jr., D. L. Harper, E. J. Sadler, T. C. McCobb, G. H. Smith, H. A. Riedemann, J. E. Crane, A. C. Minton.

JASCO STOCK FINANCIAL COMPLICATIONS

Four thousand dollars was refunded to Walter Duisberg of New York to obtain release of a claim based on a telegraphic agreement he had made with I.G. to take over their Jasco stock. This telegraphic offer and its acceptance were unknown to the author and had become known to Ringer just before he came to the Hague. He mentioned it there but said it could be neglected because it obviously was a mistake on both sides. Duisberg had not been informed that he would have to pay off the large Hambros loan referred to in the Hague Agreement before he could get possession of the stock, and even more basic was the fact that any sale of the Jasco stock to a third party without change of the Jasco agreement would have created impracticable working conditions for the company. It seemed clear that none of the people concerned in this Duisberg proposal knew the facts about the stock or the underlying contract situation and that it would be gladly abandoned when the facts were known. This conclusion was correct, but the I.G. people in Berlin who had made this mess were reluctant to try to explain it to the foreign exchange control office of their government in order to get the necessary permission to repay Duisberg in dollars. Rather than let the whole Jasco settlement drag indefinitely on this account Standard repaid Duisberg directly.

Thirty-seven thousand five hundred pounds sterling had also to be advanced by Standard to the British bank, Hambros, Ltd., which was holding the Jasco stock and other I.G. collateral against an earlier loan. This advance was later deducted by Standard from other sums due I.G. and thus was in effect paid by them.

STATEMENTS OF GOODRICH AND GOODYEAR COMPANIES
ON SYNTHETIC RUBBER

Goodrich Statement

To the Special Committee of the United States Senate Investigating the National Defense Program.

MEMBERS OF THE COMMITTEE: My associates in The B. F. Goodrich Company and I welcome this opportunity to contribute what we can to a fuller understanding of our country's rubber problem and the production of synthetic rubber.

Our people and certainly men in the fighting services are looking to us—to the government and to industry—for *just one thing*, and that is *performance*.

What we have been dealing with in respect to supplies of rubber is a situation entirely without precedent. But, as Mr. Jesse Jones has explained to you, a program for the production of synthetic rubber has been formulated and all our energies must be concentrated on its fulfillment. We have been trying to find the right path through an uncharted field. This has demanded new kinds of cooperation between many different groups,—the government, the branches of service, many different industrial organizations, individual research specialists, and teams of production and engineering personnel.

I feel certain that we have now come out of the underbrush and that we can see the road ahead. Let us move forward as rapidly as is humanly possible.

Because we shall still be dealing with entirely new situations in creating a full-scale industry to produce 700,000 tons of synthetic rubber a year, we should make the most of the experience gained from the preliminary steps that we have taken. My remarks will, I hope, be helpful in that sense.

Blessed with the highest standard of living ever known to mankind, we have accumulated 29,000,000 cars and 5,000,000 trucks and established our normal ways of living on their use. But we had not provided for their operation an unfailing domestic supply of the all important raw material, rubber.

There was not *one* reason for this, but *two*. We believed that we could prevent anyone from interrupting the trade which in 1940 brought from the Far East to this country nearly 800,000 tons of natural rubber. Normally our imports from the Far East represent 97% of all the rubber that we use.

But equally important was the fact that the United States was not sufficiently prepared to believe that synthetic rubber offered a practical alternative to natural rubber. In other words, we as a nation did not think that we should need insurance; and had not been fully convinced that such insurance existed, ready to be put into practice.

The B. F. Goodrich Company has earnestly endeavored to correct both of these conditions. I believe that it would be helpful for me to sketch briefly what we have done.

In our democracy such an undertaking requires an abundance of research skill and industrial resources, and also a determination and willingness *to acquaint the American people with the program*. It means devoting time and energy to a *basic responsibility*, —of giving freely to the people and to their elected representatives, the information and such recommendations as should be made in the public interest. This The B. F. Goodrich Company has endeavored to do. And here is some of the evidence of what our own organization has done to develop American synthetic rubber.

The largest plant in the United States now in commercial operation in the manufacture of butadiene type synthetic rubber is at one of the plants of The B. F. Goodrich Company. This plant was originally engineered and built by B. F. Goodrich without government aid to operate under patents and technique developed by our company. It was later turned over to Hycar Chemical Company, a corporation jointly owned by Phillips Petroleum Company and B. F. Goodrich. This plant has a present capacity of 7,000 long tons per annum, and it is now producing at close to capacity.

This production is the result of over fifteen years of continuous effort on the part of our own laboratories and manufacturing organization. In 1926, Dr. Waldo L. Semon, our director of synthetic rubber research, under whose direction our butadiene rubbers have been brought to a commercial basis, first experimented with the manufacture of dienes and their polymerization to produce synthetic rubber.

He continued to concentrate on the broad problem, but it was a long and painstaking study. The years required to work out scientific problems are not surprising to those familiar with research work, though the layman might well become impatient or discouraged.

There was then practically no information available on the manufacture of butadiene rubbers except the meager information set forth in the German I. G. Farbenindustrie Buna patents and a few published articles. Thus B. F. Goodrich was faced with the problem of developing butadiene copolymer rubbers by tedious experimentation covering all the complex processes and techniques involved in the manufacture of such rubbers.

By 1935 the work of the B. F. Goodrich laboratories had progressed to the point where Dr. Semon recommended to the company that increased facilities be provided for the commercial development of butadiene rubbers. By this time he was able to satisfy himself of the practical possibilities that were inherent in the field of synthetic rubber.

In 1936, the company decided to incur a very substantial expense in establishing a separate research laboratory devoted solely to research in the synthetic rubber field. This laboratory was organized under the direction of Dr. Semon, with four experienced scientists as associates.

The following year, 1937, the project was expanded and eight accomplished organic chemists were devoting their time in our laboratory entirely to the development of commercial varieties of butadiene synthetic rubbers.

In 1938, construction was started on a pilot plant. This plant was completed in 1939 with a capacity of 100 pounds of synthetic rubber per day. These facilities not only made possible synthesis of the rubber, but we also built equipment for the production of our own butadiene, as we wanted to be able to develop the process right through from the basic raw materials. Meanwhile, the laboratory work was further intensified and by the end of the year 1939, fourteen skilled B. F. Goodrich chemists and chemical engineers were devoting their full time to the synthetic rubber project.

By 1940, we had fully developed two distinct types of butadiene copolymer synthetic rubber, a tire rubber and an oil resistant specialty rubber, neither of which infringed any of the German I. G. Buna rubber patents. A commercial synthetic rubber plant was completed in that year, which had a capacity of six tons per day, or about 2,000 tons a year, and had facilities for making each of the two distinct types of butadiene copolymer synthetic rubbers.

On June 5, 1940, the B. F. Goodrich Company announced its new synthetic rubber under the trade names "Liberty Rubber" and "Ameripol," signifying the American polymer, and we displayed tires made from it as the first synthetic rubber passenger car tires to be offered for sale to the public in this country.

We had two distinct objectives in mind. The first was to challenge America's scientists to speed up the development of American-made rubber that might some day be desperately needed. The second was to focus national attention on the dangerously low stocks of natural rubber on hand in this country. On that June day in 1940, stocks on hand in the United States totalled only 148,881 tons. On January 1 of this year, stocks in the country had been increased to 535,000 tons. Full credit must be given to the government and the Rubber Reserve Company, an agency of the R. F. C., for the effectiveness with which this back log of natural rubber was accumulated. These reserve stocks make it possible for us to manufacture the war materials that we vitally need, and by the strictest conservation to bridge the gap until volume production of synthetic rubber can be obtained.

Beginning in the early summer of 1940, a few thousand of these B. F. Goodrich tires in which Ameripol replaced more than 50% of the rubber normally used, were sold to cooperative citizens and corporations at a price approximately 30% higher than the price of first quality natural rubber tires—due to the higher cost of the synthetic rubber. Many favorable reports have been received from the purchasers.

A file of photostats of letters from users of these Ameripol tires, which bear out the above statement, is attached, also a copy of an advertisement which we have published as part of our continuing policy of giving to the public the facts which we believe will be of value to them in supporting the government's program. The committee may also like to see a photograph of one of these tires which has been in use by the American Airlines Inc. on a station wagon where the service is generally far more severe than on passenger cars. This Ameripol Silvertown Tire, Serial #5496702911, was mounted by American Airlines, Inc., New York Municipal Airport, New York City, and has been driven

24,127½ miles. It was in daily service until removed so that it could be loaned to us to be exhibited to your committee.

Our company has also made and successfully tested passenger car tires in which our synthetic rubber replaced all of the natural rubber ordinarily used, except for approximately one ounce in insulation around the bead wire.

I would like to summarize here the important facts of the technical and production part of our program:

First,—The B. F. Goodrich Company has independently developed
    (A) a tire-rubber, and
    (B) an oil-resistant rubber

Second,—With our technical information and "know-how," a commercial plant was constructed without government aid, as previously mentioned, which is now actually producing at the rate of approximately 7,000 tons per year.

Third,—The B. F. Goodrich Company had before June, 1940, worked out also with its own resources and in its own laboratories the technique for the manufacture of butadiene-styrene type synthetic rubbers, so that when the government asked for the manufacture of butadiene-styrene synthetic tire rubber, the B. F. Goodrich Company had the "know-how" which it has given to the government together with its patents and technical information for making synthetic rubber for use in tires.

Fourth,—The B. F. Goodrich Company has already filed some 160 patent applications directed to novel features of its work, including some essential improvements resulting in higher quality synthetic rubbers. It has in course of preparation some 100 more applications. The B. F. Goodrich Company's patent position is strong because it covers real inventions relevant to actual manufacturing operations, all of which have been made available to the government without royalty return for use in the present War Effort.

As mentioned earlier, we understood it to be a part of our responsibility to inform the American people about the progress of our development, and to give every assistance to the government in converting this proven scientific accomplishment into effective insurance against a possible cutting-off of our normal supplies of crude rubber.

While our organization has been hard at work on the product itself, therefore our company has aggressively urged to the government and to the people the formulation of a sound synthetic rubber program.

On June 14, 1940, I appeared before the Committee on Military Affairs of the United States Senate at a hearing on a Bill to Provide For the Defense of the People of the United States (S. 4082), and there presented the desirability of the government sponsoring a commercial synthetic rubber plant having a capacity of 100 tons a day or 36,000 tons a year, stating that B. F. Goodrich would be willing to undertake the engineering and construction of such a plant and furnish the technical skill to complete the construction of such a plant within a year. We further recommended that in addition to this plant it would be desirable to establish one or more other plants of like capacity to be competitively operated.

We believe that progress could be made most rapidly by utilizing the spirit of competition in the service of the government program.

I should like to emphasize here the reason why we have consistently recommended government financing of large-scale "stand-by" plants for synthetic rubber production. Our company has invested a great deal of capital in the research and development work necessary to undertake the production of synthetic rubber. We have also created with our own capital modest productive capacity, but this was feasible because we can make the special purpose type of synthetic rubber which is of such superior qualities for many uses that its high production cost is justified.

In 1939, a total of 1,700 tons of special purpose rubber was consumed in the United States; in 1940, 4,000 tons, and in 1941, 12,000 to 15,000 tons.

It is an altogether different problem to replace the 600,000 tons of rubber needed in a normal year to make tires and many other staple products. The price per pound of rubber has been less than 3 cents as recently as 1933. This was a year prior to the adoption of the last international rubber regulation plan which remained in force until the rubber plantations were captured. Although the potential production of the plantations totalled 1,600,000 tons, world consumption has averaged just over 1,000,000 tons for the last three years.

The synthetic rubber from which the Ameripol tires were made cost nearly 60 cents a pound. I testified before the Senate

Military Affairs Committee that we believed that in plants having a capacity of 36,000 tons a year synthetic rubber for tires could be produced for as low as 25 cents a pound including amortization of the plants. Private industry in considering the financing of such large-scale plants would have to take a long range view and recognize that it would have to face competition with the price at which natural rubber could sell with unrestricted production. Rubber grown on the Eastern plantations could normally be sold commercially in New York at a price of 10 or 12 cents a pound or about 10 cents a pound under the average New York *market* price for the last two years.

Based on the United States' 1941 rubber consumption, this differential of 10 cents a pound would amount to $171,668,000. An added cost of even 1 cent a pound would amount to $17,166,000.

Moreover, in tires and other rubber products, rubber represents a large proportion of the cost, which magnifies the uneconomic spread between the price at which synthetic can be made and the price at which natural rubber can profitably be sold.

Following our recommendation to the Senate Committee on Military Affairs, The B. F. Goodrich Company submitted on July 5, 1940, a formal proposal to Mr. Clarence Francis of the Advisory Commission of the Council of National Defense for the engineering and building of two or more government-financed plants each having an annual capacity of 36,000 tons, one of these plants to be constructed and operated by the B. F. Goodrich Company.

Since that time, our company has submitted a number of other proposals to the government, urging the government sponsorship of "standby" synthetic rubber plants, and on May 1, 1941, presented to government officials a summary of America's rubber position and recommended the construction of government-financed standby plants having a combined capacity of 100,000 to 300,000 long tons per year. This presentation was summarized in the form of charts which have been mounted on an easel for ready reference. A copy of it, reduced in size, accompanies this statement.

On December 19, 1941, B. F. Goodrich and others entered into an agreement with the Rubber Reserve Company, making fully available to Rubber Reserve and operators for Rubber Reserve, without any royalty return to B. F. Goodrich, both the patents and the "know-how" of B. F. Goodrich, even though the B. F. Goodrich patents and "know-how" with respect to synthetic rubber were at least as valuable as the patent rights and "know-how" of any other in this field.

We have cooperated closely with the Rubber Reserve Company not only in the establishment of government financed synthetic rubber plants, but also in the building up of an adequate stockpile of rubber in this country and the conservation of it.

On January 26, 1942, B. F. Goodrich set forth in a series of charts, assembled in easel form for convenience, the results of an exhaustive investigation, the purpose of which was to show the absolute necessity of the greater conservation of rubber and rubber products, and in which are outlined the projected rubber requirements of the United Nations and the probable sources of rubber to meet these requirements. A copy of this analysis is also enclosed for your examination.

I do not want to appear unduly optimistic about the progress that we have made. We still have a lot to learn about synthetic rubber. Frankly, the problem of making satisfactory truck tires with synthetic rubber is still a big one. We have made strides and will reach that goal, if day-and-night effort brings the results in the weeks and months ahead that it has in the past. We are told that Germany has not yet successfully used synthetic rubber 100% in truck tires. We are challenged to accomplish this before the end of 1942.

We must rush the building of synthetic plants without losing a moment. Synthetic rubber production estimates have been made for the years 1943 and 1944. But these estimates might be upset by shortage of structural materials, transportation delays and shortage of experienced engineering personnel. The Government and industry must organize so that work will proceed with the utmost speed, overcoming all hindrances. It has been indicated that necessary priorities will be given; and this, of course, is fundamental.

Speed in the erection of plants to produce butadiene and styrene is of vital importance, for these are the basic materials required for this program. We must have adequate production of the necessary raw materials from the chemical and petroleum industries in order for the synthesis plants, which are the responsibility of the rubber industry, to turn out their product—synthetic rubber.

Equally important, however, is for us all to understand clearly that we have two other equally big jobs to do; One is the collection of scrap rubber so that we can fully utilize the facilities that we have for making reclaimed rubber, and the other greater conservation of rubber.

The scrap rubber situation is critical and calls for prompt and effective action. In the months and years that preceded Pearl Harbor it was not possible for anyone to appreciate fully the vital necessity of building synthetic rubber producing capacity on anything like the scale now scheduled. But today no one can fail to see the danger of failing to take the necessary action with regard to scrap rubber.

Dependence upon reclaimed rubber is a basic factor in all planning to bridge the gap until synthetic rubber begins to come in, and even thereafter, as well. In straining every fibre to make available materials to replace our lost regular supplies of crude rubber, the country has assumed that our reclaiming plants would operate at capacity, and that insofar as may be practical, this capacity would be enlarged. We can make with existing facilities 350,000 tons of reclaim a year if the scrap comes in.

But without a steady flow of scrap rubber to them, these plants cannot operate at all, or only at sharply reduced rates. The unpleasant fact is that during the first three months of this year, scrap rubber came in to the reclaiming plants at a rate of 50% below the figure needed to operate them at capacity.

Under present circumstances it is, of course, human nature for the public to hold on to old rubber, even though its useful life, except as scrap for reclaim is exhausted. This means that something more effective must be done to restore and accelerate the flow of scrap rubber to the reclaim plants.

It will take an all-out continuing nation-wide "rubber roundup" to bring in the worn and discarded rubber products that are desperately needed.

I cannot emphasize too strongly this imperative need to comb every county in this country for the scrap rubber that will help us to meet the rubber crisis. We must have reclaimed rubber to use in stretching out our crude rubber stockpile for manufacturing the war materials and vital civilian products. This part of the program must not lag. But it is lagging today, and that problem must be solved without the loss of another day.

The other big job we have to do is to intensify our program of *rubber conservation.*

In estimating future rubber consumption no provision has been made for the removal of present restrictions on tires for civilian use. Eventually products made of rubber must be replaced or vital services will break down. Workers must have transportation to and from distant war production jobs. A way must be found to keep America's automobiles and trucks—key factors in U. S. war or peace economy—on the road. We must keep *them* rolling, too.

This is the reason that we must press for further action which will make rubber available for the basic needs of the American people. Only one course is open. We need a much more intensive program of rubber conservation. This can be accomplished by the wholehearted cooperation of the government, industry, the Army and Navy, and private owners of automotive equipment. The rationing of civilian tires was a prompt and necessary move, but there are other possibilities which will help to accomplish the objective.

This nation's greatest rubber stockpile is in the form of unworn mileage in tires and tubes now in possession of owners of trucks, buses, and automobiles. Over 140,000,000 tires are on rolling wheels. Spare tires and excess stocks in the hands of consumers total another 33,000,000 casings. After allowances for wear, the rubber content of these 173,000,000 tires and tubes totals around 1,200,000 long tons, nearly twice the national stockpile of new rubber. Then there is the stockpile of rubber products belonging to the fighting services. Intelligent care in the use of this stockpile of unknown mileage can keep wheels rolling longer than we think.

Cutting down driving speeds is the most important of all rubber conservation measures. The slower tires are driven the more mileage they will give. Speed causes heat and increases abrasion, and thus wears out tires quickly. For example, if motorists who used to drive 60 miles per hour on the highway, will cut down their speed to 30 miles per hour, they can get almost three times as much tire mileage. This means that months of service can be added to the life of tires now running. Millions will be astonished to find the added mileage they will get by resolutely holding down car speed. Moreover, lower speeds prevent tire carcasses from being burned up prematurely by heat which is generated within a tire at high speed. This is the great hope for the private motorist. If the carcass is well preserved it is good for one, two and sometimes three retreadings.

Tire users will also do well to memorize the magic words "Inflate-Rotate"; they are the key to the continued use of our cars. Keep air pressures up and rotate tires including the spare from wheel to wheel every 5,000 miles or less.

We can conserve by controlling inventories of rubber products. Great care must be taken so that we do not manufacture into the form of finished products that are not essential, rubber and other materials that may have to be used for essential purposes later. Attention to reducing waste in manufacturing plants should be intensified.

We must continue to review designs and specifications, making sure that necessary rubber products are suitably made but with the minimum quantity of rubber.

We must encourage service and repair, thus greatly prolonging the life of rubber products.

We must make the greatest saving that American ingenuity can obtain by using reclaimed rubber, chemicals, and substitutes for rubber wherever possible. Our laboratories must work with redoubled energy to make available as rapidly as possible whatever contributions science and long years of experience can make to the solution of the problems caused by our inability to obtain normal supplies of crude rubber.

Only if all of these measures are taken aggressively now, will sufficient rubber and reclaimed rubber be available to keep necessary civilian cars and trucks in operation. Naturally military needs will have the first call on synthetic rubber, just as is the case with natural rubber and reclaimed rubber.

Winning this war is the biggest job that America has ever tackled. And fighting the rubber problem through to a satisfactory solution is the biggest job that we have ever faced on the home front. Working against time we now have to replace America's No 1 import, crude rubber. By sheer *will-power* we must save every scrap of rubber until we make something to take its place.

The Congress of the United States and the officials of our government are fully alert to this challenge. The people—130,000,000 strong—will, I feel sure, join them in the full cooperation which alone can bring victory.

[Signed]   JOHN L. COLLYER,
President, The B. F. Goodrich Company.

Goodyear Statement

In October, 1933, we were first shown a sample of Buna rubber by Mr. Haslam of the Standard Oil Development Co. It was reported that this rubber gave tread wear superior to natural rubber and this fact was of great interest to us because no previous synthetic had been anywhere near as good as the natural product. The reported oil and gasoline resistance was also of interest, although the requirement for such rubber was, at that time rather small.

On November 6th, we again visited the S O Development offices and tried to interest that company in allowing us to work with them in their tire problems with Buna rubber. No interest was evidenced by Standard in this proposal and we were unable to create any in the next few months, for in February, 1934, we were given a definite rejection.

The research problem of making Buna was studied and in November, 1934, after some attempts to locate a source of butadiene, laboratory investigation was begun on methods of making butadiene and acrylonitrile, prerequisites to the experimental preparation of Buna. Early in 1935, we were generating butadiene in laboratory glass equipment and had sufficient styrene and acrylonitrile available so we were able to carry on laboratory scale polymerization experiments. In June a somewhat larger butadiene generator was available and we were able to widen the scope of our synthetic experiments.

Early in 1935 Mr. Dinsmore visited the I. G. plant in Leverkusen and received considerable information about the properties of Buna S and Buna N. He was permitted to inspect the laboratory polymerizer, but was given little information about the process. At this time Standard advised us that it was handling the Buna rights in the U. S. However, the I. G. people were non-committal. No samples were obtained from the I. G.

In November, 1936, a five gallon pot was set up for our rubber polymerization and work was continued until the following July, when a 75 gallon kettle was installed, by which time our knowledge of the process had progressed to a point where we were confident we could duplicate the German Buna on a laboratory scale. In March, 1937, Dr. Sebrell, Goodyear Research Manager, went to Germany and visited the I. G. He was told that they were making 175 tons per month (about 6,000 tons per year). He was told that they were not ready to give a decision about licenses possibly for four months.

A tire was treaded by us with Buna S in August, 1937, and another was made with Buna N in September. In this month we finally received a shipment of about 1,000 pounds each of German Buna S and Buna N and a small amount of a variety called Buna K-85. Before the end of October, we had sent to I. G. in Frankfort, two new and two worn tires and samples of gasoline and steam hose and a gasket and piece of conveyer belt—all made from Buna type rubber, produced in our laboratories. The purpose of this was to show the I. G. that we were far enough advanced to reproduce their rubber. All through this period there was uncertainty in our minds whether I. G. or Standard would control the licensing of this type rubber. In the latter part of 1937, Goodyear took active steps to interest Dow Chemical in the production of butadiene and acrylonitrile.

On January 4, 1938, the first tires were made wholly of Goodyear synthetic. On February 7th, Dr. Duisberg, patent representative in New York for I. G., was informed of our progress and three days later was given a wholly synthetic tire to send to Germany.

In May, 1938, a series of conferences were held with Standard and I. G. representatives in New York, which did not result in any progress. Dinsmore attended a technical convention in London and, in early June, again visited I. G. in Leverkusen. On this occasion he learned that the Germans were devoting all their attention to Buna S because it was easier to process than Buna N. A new building had just been completed for the purpose of adapting Buna to production processes. Dinsmore went through this building, which was only partly equipped, and noticed that the Buna was causing many difficulties in tire processing.

In October an adequate sample of Goodyear synthetic was furnished Dr. Russell of Standard, for test purposes. In early November, Mr. Howard having just returned from Germany, a conference was proposed, but was later postponed by him. Mr.

Bedford of Standard advised that Dr. ter Meer of I. G. would be in Akron December 12th. Messrs. ter Meer and Hochschwender came and discussed the Buna situation. No definite assurances were given as to the possibilities of a license and disclosure of the important operating technique.

At this time, as far as tires were concerned, we were still chiefly attracted to Buna as an interesting technical development. We were hopeful that the expanding demand for oil-resistant rubber, might permit us to commercialize Buna N while we carried on our development of tire rubber. We considered that the probable cost of these rubbers, would be too high, relative to natural rubber, to justify their use, except for special properties which natural rubber does not have. In tires, this had to do mainly with wear-resistance. Hence we worked mostly with tread compounds and with the thought of getting the best wear. It was not until Germany began to gain complete control of Europe, in 1940, that we thought of the Buna type rubbers as all-purpose substitutes. It therefore turned out that our work on producing softer rubber of the oil-resisting and wear resisting types, and our work to produce high-yields and fast production, was not altogether applicable to the type of rubber ultimately needed for an all-purpose war substitute.

Through 1939, then, we continued our experimental work with the objects just stated, in mind. We investigated large number of new polymers, developed by our Research Chemists, and studied and improved the process of manufacture. We momentarily expected a definite proposal from Standard and, in the latter part of November, such a proposal was finally submitted. Negotiations for modification of the proposed license terms were rather active into October, 1940, and continued until January, 1941. No agreement was reached as Goodyear objected to the high royalties and other terms which it considered unreasonable.

In June 1940 the Senate committee on Military Affairs had a hearing, at which Mr. Collyer of Goodrich and Mr. Bridgewater of duPont testified regarding the synthetic rubber situation. Subsequently a number of conversations were held between various representatives of the rubber industry and Mr. Francis' Defense Committee. This culminated in a meeting on Aug. 7, 1940 with Mr. Francis' Committee, and officials and technical representatives of Goodyear, Goodrich, Firestone, U. S. Rubber, General Tire, Shell, Standard Oil of N. J., Phillips, Dow, Carbide & Carbon and

United Gas Improvement. Plans for producing 100,000 tons per year of synthetic were discussed. Various companies indicated how much rubber they would be willing to make. Problems of financing the plants and arranging for commercial use of the rubber were discussed. Some preliminary engineering plans and cost estimates were requested. Goodyear furnished figures, as requested. On August 27th, the second industry meeting was switched over to Mr. Schram of the R. F. C. It was explained that the reason for this was because the R. F. C. had the mechanism for financing plants and for handling rubber through its Rubber Reserve Co. Mr. Litchfield recommended to Mr. Schram a minimum program of 50,000 tons per year to enable industry to learn how to make and use the synthetic. Mr. Schram said he thought the government should finance the program.

Having been told that we should investigate raw materials supply for our own part in the synthetic program, we were busy for the next few months trying to work out arrangements for butadiene and other materials, completing and revising plant and equipment designs, according to each new suggestion coming out of Washington and submitting various cost estimates.

On December 2nd, 1940, we received unofficial advice that the government then favored four 10,000 ton plants, to be financed 25% by the operators and 75% by the R. F. C. It was said that the government preferred to deal with one party, for both raw materials and rubber, for each 10,000 ton unit. Hence, Goodyear explored both sub-contracting and joint subsidiaries with Oil and Chemical companies. A joint company with Dow Chemical was finally worked out.

Meantime in November, 1940, Goodyear completed and put into operation a synthetic plant for producing a ton of rubber per day. This plant enabled us to provide rubber on a production scale and test our producing methods and develop them more thoroughly.

The people we talked to in the government seemed to agree that an adequate educational program was sound, should be sponsored and financed by the government and should be carried out at once. We momentarily expected action and endeavored to supply all information and estimates as rapidly as possible. Nothing definite occurred until March 28, 1941, when Mr. Klossner of Rubber Reserve submitted a request for proposals to erect four 2,500 ton plants, housed in buildings capable of taking 10,000 ton equipment. We were told to make no provision for raw materials as an adequate supply was available. In January, 1941, work was started by us upon the construction of an additional private synthetic rubber plant.

On May 15, 1941, Goodyear signed an agreement of lease with DPC and started at once to get approval of site and plant design, so work could be started. At the request of Reserve, this agreement was made with Goodyear, for rubber polymerization only.

No provision was made for butadiene. The Goodyear-Dow Company was out. Almost at once, Mr. Deupree of OPM, began to hold meetings with the industry to discuss enlargement of the authorized plants. By that time, Goodyear was seriously alarmed about the trend of the war and urgently recommended (1) that the program be immediately expanded to 100,000 tons or more and (2) that raw materials plants be authorized at once. It was pointed out, by us, that the raw materials plants cost more and took longer to build and, in the case of butadiene, the processes were not so well developed as in the case of synthetic rubber itself. In early July, we were authorized to increase our plant to 10,000 tons capacity. On September 4th we were told that contracts for butadiene were about to be awarded to Carbide, Standard and Celanese. From this time on we received very little information about the progress of raw materials except to be assured that they would be available when needed. In September, 1941, we completed our additional private plant for the production of 2,000 tons of rubber per year. This plan cost us several hundred thousand dollars. It enabled us to enlarge our production experience, train needed men and to provide essential oil resistant rubber.

September 11, 1941, Goodyear received a notice from Jasco Inc. (Standard I. G.) that we were infringing their synthetic rubber patents. In October and November revised figures were worked out for the Rubber Reserve to conform with the types of synthetic rubber which had been agreed upon as more or less standard for government plants. Revisions of the operating agreement for our 10,000 ton unit were also made.

On December 14 Mr. Litchfield attended a meeting in Washington for the purpose of discussing plans for doubling or tripling the synthetic plant project. Fast action was promised. Two days later Rubber Reserve entered into an agreement with Goodyear, Goodrich, Firestone, U. S. Rubber and Standard Oil, whereby there was to be a complete exchange of information and patent rights on synthetic rubber for the duration of the emergency. Our initial contribution to this pool consisted of 65 separate inventions, 10 covered by patents and 55 by patent applications, for which we did not request and will not receive any compensation or royalties.

On January 17, 1942, Goodyear was authorized by Rubber Reserve to increase the capacity of its DPC synthetic rubber plant from 10,000 to 30,000 tons per year. The first unit of the plant will be ready for operation in May, 1942.

This chronological history of Goodyear's synthetic efforts is necessarily limited to the most essential details. It would be difficult to present an accurate account of the weeks which were spent in negotiating and re-negotiating agreements to produce government rubber in conformity with each change of plan proposed by government authorities or the painstaking work which was done in designing, testing and revising equipment for large scale production with which we had had limited experience.

Although our negotiations with Standard Oil and the I. G. were time-consuming and fruitless, we must, in fairness state that, had they been successful, they would have resulted only in a somewhat larger commercial plant for oil-resistant rubber—perhaps 5,000-10,000 tons per year. This would have done relatively little to expedite the tire rubber program, which is now of major interest.

On the other hand, the bottle-neck of the government program has been, and is today, the production of butadiene. Lack of this material would have made any large expansion of private rubber plants worthless, and failure to keep pace in this respect with the development of rubber polymerization must necessarily add many months to our rubber program.

PARTIES TO GENERAL AGREEMENT ON EXCHANGE AND USE OF
TECHNICAL INFORMATION RELATING TO BUTADIENE

Rubber Reserve Company
Universal Oil Products Company
Standard Oil Development Company
Jasco, Incorporated
Shell Development Company
The M. W. Kellogg Company
Humble Oil and Refining Company
Koppers Company
Koppers United Company
Shell Oil Company, Incorporated

Shell Union Oil Corporation
Carbide and Carbon Chemicals Corporation
Phillips Petroleum Company
The Lummus Company
Celanese Corporation of America
Standard Oil Company of Louisiana
Hycar Chemical Company
The B. F. Goodrich Company
The Dow Chemical Company
The United Gas Improvement Company

Houdry Process Corporation

PARTIES TO AGREEMENT ON EXCHANGE AND USE OF TECHNICAL
INFORMATION RELATING TO STYRENE

Rubber Reserve Company
Universal Oil Products Company
Standard Oil Development Company
Jasco, Inc.
Koppers Company

Koppers United Company
Monsanto Chemical Company
Carbide and Carbon Chemicals Corporation
Phillips Petroleum Company
The Lummus Company
The Dow Chemical Company

THE PRESIDENT'S LETTER OF MARCH 20, 1942

Released from
The White House   March 28, 1942

On March 20th, the President received from the Attorney General, the Secretary of War, the Secretary of the Navy and Thurman Arnold, the following signed memorandum:

"March 20, 1942
"Dear Mr. President:

"The undersigned have been considering for some time the problem presented by the fact that some of the pending court investigations, suits and prosecutions under the anti-trust statutes by the Department of Justice, if continued, will interfere with the production of war materials.

"In the present all-out effort to produce quickly and uninterruptedly a maximum amount of weapons of warfare, such court investigations, suits, and prosecutions unavoidably consume the time of executives and employees of those corporations which are engaged in war work. In those cases we believe that continuing such prosecutions at this time will be contrary to the national interest and security. It is therefore something which we seek to obviate as quickly as possible.

"On the other hand we all wish to make sure: 1. That no one who has committed a violation of law shall escape ultimate investigation and prosecution; 2. That no such person shall even now be permitted to postpone investigation or prosecution under a false pretext that his undivided time is necessary to the war effort —in other words that it must be preponderantly clear that the progress of the war effort is being impeded; and, 3. That no one who has sought actually to defraud the government shall obtain any postponement of investigation or prosecution in any event.

"Accordingly we have worked out the following procedure, subject to your approval.

"Each pending and future Federal court investigation, prosecution or suit under the anti-trust laws will be carefully studied and examined as soon as possible by the Attorney General, and the Secretary of War or the Secretary of the Navy respectively. If the Attorney General and the Secretary of War or the Secretary of the Navy come to the conclusion that the court investigation, prosecution or suit will not seriously interfere with the all-out prosecution of the war, the Attorney General will proceed. If they agree that it will interfere; or if after study and examination they disagree, then, upon receipt of a letter from the Secretary of War or the Secretary of the Navy stating that in his opinion the investigation, suit, or prosecution will seriously interfere with the war effort, the Attorney General will abide by that decision and defer his activity in that particular matter, providing, however, that he shall have the right, in such event, to lay all the facts before the President whose determination, of course, shall be final. In each case the action finally taken will be made public.

"The deferment or adjustment of the investigation, suit, or prosecution will not, however, mean the exoneration of the individual or corporation, or the discontinuance of the proceeding. As soon as it appears that it will no longer interfere with war production, the Attorney General will proceed.

"To make sure that no one escapes by the running of the statute of limitations, we shall request Congress to pass an appropriate extension of the statute.

"Under no circumstances will there be any suspension or postponement of prosecution for any actual fraud committed against the Government.

"We feel that this arrangement will adequately protect the public interest.

"Respectfully yours,

(Signed)   FRANCIS BIDDLE
              Attorney General

"   HENRY L. STIMSON
              Secretary of War

"   FRANK KNOX
              Secretary of the Navy

"   THURMAN ARNOLD
              Thurman Arnold"

On the same day, March 20th, the President in identic letters addressed to the Attorney General, the Secretary of War and the Secretary of the Navy, notified them of his approval of the procedure outlined in the above memorandum.

The President's letter reads:

"March 20, 1942

"I approved of the procedure outlined in your memorandum to me dated March 20, 1942. If it is true that any substantial slowing-up of war production is being occasioned by anti-trust suits, prosecutions or court investigations then the war effort must come first and everything else must wait. For unless that effort is successful, the anti-trust laws, as indeed all American institutions, will become quite academic.

"No one, of course, should be permitted to escape ultimate prosecution for any violation of law. I am sure that the Departments of Justice, War and Navy will all cooperate so that the needs of the war will not be hampered by these court investigations, suits or prosecutions, but that at the same time the crisis of war will not be used as a means of avoiding just penalties for any wrongdoing. In other words, it must be made very clear that the war effort is being impeded. No right-minded person, or any one who is conscious of what is at stake, should use the nation's extremities as an excuse to violate any statute.

"Nor indeed should there be any deferment or adjournment of any court investigations, prosecution or suit unless, after a study and examination with the Attorney General in each specific case, the Secretary of War or of the Navy is satisfied that the war effort will be jeopardized at this time unless such course is followed.

"I note from your memorandum that proper steps will be taken to avoid the running of the statute of limitations in any case; and that under no circumstances will there be any delay in the prosecution of acts involving actual fraud upon the Government.

"I also heartily approve your intention of making public each determination arrived at by you in accordance with your memorandum. The American people should be informed of each step in their war effort, excepting, of course, any information which may in any way help the enemy in his attempt to destroy us.

"While every precaution will be taken to prevent anyone from escaping prosecution if he has violated the anti-trust statutes, whether he is now engaged in war work or not, we must keep our eyes fixed now upon the one all-important primary task—to produce more materials at a greater speed. In other words we shall give our attention to first things first.

"Very sincerely yours,

(Signed) "FRANKLIN D. ROOSEVELT"

CONSENT DECREE OF MARCH 25, 1942

(PREAMBLE)

The complainant, United States of America, having filed its complaint herein on March 25, 1942; the defendants having appeared and filed their answers to such complaint denying the substantive allegations thereof; all parties hereto by their attorneys herein having severally consented to the entry of this final decree herein without trial or adjudication of any issue of fact or law herein and without admission by any party in respect of any such issue;

Now, therefore, before any testimony has been taken herein, and without trial or adjudication of any issue of fact or law herein, and upon consent of all parties hereto, it is hereby

ORDERED, ADJUDGED AND DECREED as follows:

May 8, 1942

HON. CLAUDE R. WICKARD,
Secretary of Agriculture,
Washington, D. C.

MY DEAR MR. SECRETARY: In view of your statement today, I am writing to inquire whether this company can be of assistance to you in your consideration of the use of agricultural alcohol as a raw material for the manufacture of butadiene for rubber production. I am advised by our technical organization that we have processes for the production of butadiene from alcohol through the aldehyde-aldol-butylene glycol route. Although we have had no commercial experience with this process, our technical people are confident that it is a sound operation. Our own estimate of about 2.2 pounds of butadiene per gallon of alcohol seems to be about the same as those which have been published in relation to the Carbide and Carbon Company's process and the process of the Publicker Alcohol Company; but more detailed examination and comparison would be necessary to determine the relative merits of the three processes. The other two processes are certainly more modern and perhaps cheaper than our own, but under present conditions the most important point is not the exact cost but the time required to obtain the production and the amount of critical materials required for the plants. This is a complicated question which only the Government authorities could pass on intelligently after a full review of all the facts.

If it should appear that our process above referred to, or any of our other processes, would be of any value in the program of immediate production of synthetic rubber from agricultural alcohol they will be available, royalty free, for the duration of the war, and we will render all possible technical assistance in connection with the program.

Very truly yours,

(Signed) W. S. FARISH

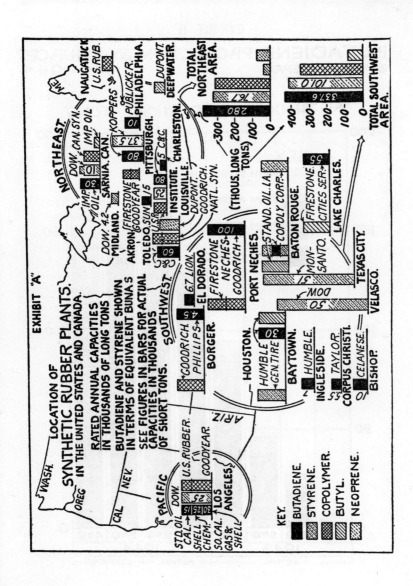

EXHIBIT "B"

BUTADIENE · PRODUCTION · BY · SOURCES
BY · QUARTERS   1943 – 1944

IN · THOUSANDS · OF · SHORT · TONS

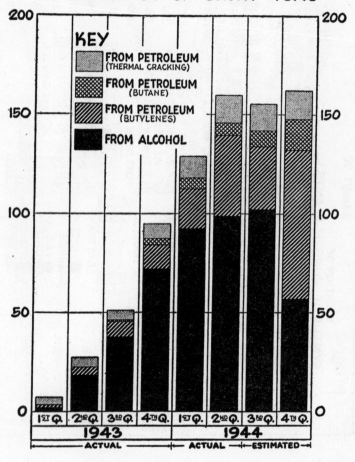

EXHIBIT "C"

ESTIMATED SYNTHETIC RUBBER PRODUCTION*
OF BUNA S, BUTYL, NEOPRENE AND BUNA N
BY QUARTERS, JANUARY 1943 – JUNE 1945

*INCLUDES CAPACITIES OF PRIVATE PLANTS

	1943					1944					1945		
	1ST	2ND	3RD	4TH	YEAR TOTAL	1ST	2ND	3RD	4TH	YEAR TOTAL	1ST	2ND	6 MO. TOTAL
BUNA·S	3,102	18,792	56,741	106,146	184,781	145,641	186,035	185,700	195,000	712,376	195,000	195,000	390,000
BUTYL	35	393	364	581	1,373	3,081	3,928	4,560	9,590	21,159	12,430	15,120	27,550
NEOPRENE	4,372	5,853	10,049	13,329	33,603	13,962	14,991	14,250	14,250	57,453	16,250	17,250	33,500
BUNA·N	2,977	3,335	4,063	4,112	14,487	4,399	4,050	6,550	5,050	20,049	4,850	4,850	9,700
TOTAL SYNTHETIC	10,486	28,373	71,217	124,168	234,244	167,083	209,004	211,060	223,890	811,037	228,530	232,220	460,750

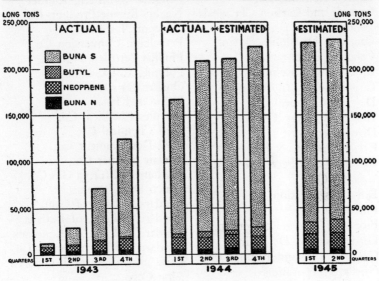

LIST OF COMPANIES RECEIVING CHEMICAL AND METALLURGICAL
ENGINEERING "AWARD FOR CHEMICAL ENGINEERING
ACHIEVEMENT."

American Cyanamid Co.
E. B. Badger and Sons Co.
Barium Reduction Co.
Bell Telephone Laboratories
Bigler Chemical Co.
Blaw-Knox Company
C. F. Braun and Co.
Buffalo Electrochemical Co.
Canton Refining Co.
Carbide and Carbon Chemicals Corp.
Catalytic Development Co.
Celanese Corporation
Cities Service Refining Co.
Copolymer Corporation
Davison Chemical Co.
Dewey & Almy Chemical Co.
Dow Chemical Co.
E. I. du Pont de Nemours & Co.
Eastern States Petroleum & Refining Co.
Ethyl Corporation
Filtros, Inc.
Firestone Tire & Rubber Co.
Ford, Bacon & Davis, Inc.
General Tire and Rubber Co.
Girdler Corporation
B. F. Goodrich Co.
Goodyear Tire & Rubber Co.
Harshaw Chemical Co.
Hercules Powder Co.
Hooker Electro Chemical Co.
Houdry Process Corp.

Humble Oil and Refining Co.
Hycar Chemical Co.
M. W. Kellogg Co.
Koppers United Co.
Lion Oil and Refining Co.
Lummus Company
Monsanto Chemical Co.
National Carbide Co.
National Synthetic Rubber
Neches Butane Products Co.
Newport Industries
Petroleum Conversion Co.
Phillips Petroleum Co.
Polymer Corp., Ltd.
Quaker Oats Co.
Rohm and Haas
Sharples Chemical Co.
Shell Chemical Co.
Shell Development Co.
Sinclair Rubber Co.
Southern California Gas Co.
Stanco Distributors
Standard Oil Co. of Calif.
Standard Oil Co. of Indiana
Standard Oil Co. of Louisiana
Standard Oil Development Co.
Stone and Webster Engineering Corp.
Sun Oil Co.
Taylor Refining Co.
Thiokol Corporation
United Gas Improvement Co.
United States Rubber Co.
Universal Oil Products Co.

Westvaco Chlorine Products Corp.

INDEX

301